BASIC CONCEPTS OF NUCLEAR CHEMISTRY

Selected Topics in Modern Chemistry

SERIES EDITORS

Professor Harry H. Sisler
Department of Chemistry
University of Florida

Professor Calvin A. VanderWerf
Department of Chemistry
University of Kansas

PUBLISHED

EYRING AND EYRING—*Modern Chemical Kinetics*

KIEFFER—*The Mole Concept in Chemistry*

MOELLER—*The Chemistry of the Lanthanides*

OVERMAN—*Basic Concepts of Nuclear Chemistry*

RYSCHKEWITSCH—*Chemical Bonding and the Geometry of Molecules*

SISLER—*Chemistry in Non-Aqueous Solvents*

VANDERWERF—*Acids, Bases, and the Chemistry of the Covalent Bond*

(Many additional titles are in preparation.)

The fields of radiochemistry and nuclear chemistry are two of the most modern areas of chemical research. It is, therefore, highly important that chemistry students of today have an opportunity to understand and appreciate the important aspects of these two areas and that they receive adequate instruction in the basic principles which characterize radio chemical and nuclear chemical phenomena.

The author of "Basic Concepts of Nuclear Chemistry" is eminently well qualified by his experience at the Oak Ridge Institute of Nuclear Studies and by his strong interest in chemical education to provide a book which will meet this need. We believe that he has succeeded admirably in this objective. This volume is as contemporary as modern publishing procedures will allow and we are proud indeed to add it to the Reinhold SELECTED TOPICS IN MODERN CHEMISTRY series.

Harry H. Sisler
C. A. VanderWerf

BASIC CONCEPTS
OF NUCLEAR
CHEMISTRY

RALPH T. OVERMAN

Chairman, Special Training Division
Oak Ridge Institute of Nuclear Studies
Oak Ridge, Tennessee

New York
REINHOLD PUBLISHING CORPORATION
Chapman & Hall, Ltd., London

PREFACE

Nuclear chemistry as a specialization has undergone a major and rapid development in the last 20 years. Although many chemists have worked with radioactive materials since the discovery of radioactivity in 1896, most of the early "radiation chemists" or "radiochemists" concentrated on separating and examining naturally radioactive materials, with primary emphasis on the isolation and study of hitherto unknown elements. After fission was accomplished, another group of workers developed the area of fission product chemistry, where the concern was with the isolation and study of isotopes of known elements, although two unknown elements, numbers 47 and 61, were also found in the fission product mixtures. The wartime interest in nuclear matters also produced the transuranium chemists, who have extended the periodic table far beyond the range of the naturally occurring elements.

After World War II, it became apparent that radioactive materials and nuclear techniques would have a broad impact and that the basic information about them would be essential not only to chemists at all levels of study but also to a wide variety of other scientific investigators in fields ranging from medicine to engineering. This is the reason that yet another book should be placed on your bookshelf. The basic concepts of nuclear chemistry stem more from physics than from chemistry, but we may say that chemistry is the bridge across which we must walk to put the atom to work.

The material in this book is the outgrowth of a series of lectures given to various groups over a period of years. The approach was developed for our Oak Ridge courses in radio-isotope techniques, in which the participants are research workers who have not had wide experience in physics or chemistry. In addition, much of the material has been adapted for general lectures to advanced high school and undergraduate college students and has been presented at meetings of professional societies.

Out of this experience has been developed a concise treatment of the basic principles of nuclear chemistry at the level of the undergraduate college student who has some familiarity with scientific concepts and terminology. At the same time, it is hoped that the book will also be useful for workers in various scientific fields whose training did not include some of these concepts and for high school students who wish to enrich their regular course offerings.

The first two chapters are a survey of the concepts of atomic and nuclear structure necessary for an understanding of radioactivity and other nuclear phenomena. Since nuclear chemistry deals so heavily with radioactivity and the radiations from such substances, Chapter 3 is devoted to the description of how these radiations interact with matter and Chapter 4 to how they may be detected and measured; as in any analytical procedure, a knowledge of the instruments which are used in the determination of quantitative relationships is necessary. Chapter 5 treats the decay laws and statistical probability which are of considerable importance both to laboratory measurement of nuclear properties and to understanding the special characteristics of radioactivity.

Since no book of practical size can contain an adequate description of the fantastic range of applications of nuclear chemistry, the final chapter gives a few examples in the field of chemistry. Other fields could not be included, even though perhaps the greatest contribution of nuclear chemistry has been to the very difficult problems in such areas as medicine and biochemistry.

As in every effort of this kind, it is impossible to acknowledge the influence of all the people who have contributed both to the writing of the book and to the development of the concepts and analogies contained in it. However, Lawrence K. Akers and Jerry Minter gave particular help by reading the manuscript and assisting me in clarifying many of the points which I have tried to explore. I also wish to thank all the Special Training Division staff, who contributed greatly over a period of years to the development of the conceptual and pedagogical approach; the secretarial staff, including Edith Wilson, Shirley Vowell, and Mrs. E. E. Overton, who typed the manuscript; Harvey Covert and T. F. X. McCarthy, who helped read proof; and Loren K. Palmer, who prepared the drawings, reproducing my blackboard vagaries faithfully in a manner more intelligible than the original. To Dr. W. G. Pollard, the Executive Director of the Oak Ridge Institute of Nuclear Studies, goes my appreciation for his constant personal and professional support.

Finally, I should like to extend my gratitude to my family who have endured my absences from home when I was trying out my lectures on many audiences, as well as the time away from them during the preparation of the book itself.

Oak Ridge, Tennessee   RALPH T. OVERMAN
January, 1963

CONTENTS

Preface vii

1. Atomic and Nuclear Structure 1

2. Radioactivity and Nuclear Reactions 19

3. Interaction of Radiation with Matter 38

4. The Detection of Nuclear Radiation 58

5. Radioactive Decay Laws and Counting Statistics 80

6. Applications of Nuclear Chemistry 95

Selected References 111

Index 113

chapter one

ATOMIC AND NUCLEAR STRUCTURE

Nuclear Chemistry

To begin with, the term "nuclear chemistry" is a paradox. Chemical changes involve the transfer or sharing of valence electrons. However, the usual properties of nuclei—mass, atomic number, and nuclear structure—bear no direct relation to chemical reactions. Consequently, there can be no direct relationship between the chemical and nuclear properties of atoms.

On the other hand, a wide variety of phenomena are of interest to chemists either because certain nuclear properties provide new chemical tools or because differences in nuclei actually produce subtleties of chemical behavior. Thus, nuclear chemistry includes any of the relationships between atomic and nuclear structure of importance to a chemist.

In general, the nuclear chemist is concerned with those properties involving similarities and differences among the isotopes of a given element. It should be stressed that, in addition to stable isotopes, the nuclear chemist studies radioactive isotopes by the application of the various techniques of radiochemistry and radiation chemistry. We often use the term "radiochemistry" to describe work with radioactive atomic species, whereas radiation chemistry is now limited to chemical effects brought about by radiation interacting with a system.

In developing the basic concepts of nuclear chemistry, we will be concerned with nuclear structure, radiation physics, and instrumentation for the identification of various isotopes, as well as with such mathematical problems as the laws of radioactive growth and decay. We will also consider some of the chemical problems that those who work with radioactive materials must face and will suggest a few applications of nuclear chemistry to analytical chemistry. All of this information serves as the starting point for anyone entering the field of nuclear chemistry, either as a specialist or as a person wishing to add its special techniques to his training.

The Structure of the Atom

As is well known, our present concept of the atom includes the notion that the atom consists of a dense nucleus containing protons and neutrons and surrounded by electrons occupying certain positions, or following certain paths of motion. It would be very simple if we could describe the electrons as having definite kinds of motion. However, it was pointed out by Heisenberg in his statement of the uncertainty principle that it is impossible to know at the same time the energy and the position of any particle such as an electron. Any experiment designed to measure the location or the energy of an electron must change either the location or the energy in the measuring process. *Since we cannot specify the electron motion precisely, it is impossible to draw electron paths or tracks. Hence, we can speak only of the probability or relative chance of finding an electron at any given position within the atom.*

It is important to realize that a proper description of atomic or subatomic structure can be made only through the use of mathematical equations. Even so, it is worthwhile and quite common to employ what the scientist calls a "model" for descriptive purposes. The particular model he will use varies with his sophistication. The development of scientific models that are incomplete, if necessary, but still not incorrect is one of the interesting problems of scientific communications.

Finding an Electron by Quantum Mechanics. The probability of finding an electron in an atom can be deduced by means of the techniques of quantum or wave mechanics. The common method of using these mathematical techniques is to formulate the equations that describe the motions of waves and to employ them to describe the probabilities of finding atomic or subatomic particles. One of the results of describing the probability of finding an electron is shown in Fig. 1.1. This diagram illustrates the probability of finding the electron nearest the nucleus at a given point in the atom of which it is a part. The probability of locating it in a particular small region (at a given point) is shown, and it can be seen that the probability of finding this electron is highest at the center of the nucleus. The motion corresponding to this probability can be described as an oscillating motion through the nucleus, but, as we shall see later, an electron cannot be considered as a part of the nucleus.

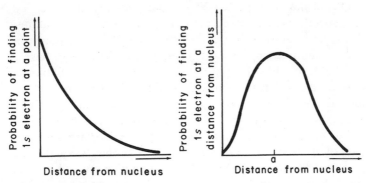

Fig. 1.1. Probability of finding a 1s electron at a given point in the atom.

Fig. 1.2. Probability of finding a 1s electron in a given shell of the atom.

On the other hand, we can show the probability of finding the electron in a particular spherical "shell" outside of the nucleus. The curve is shown in Fig. 1.2. The difference in these two diagrams is explained on the basis of the fact that although the probability of finding the electron in a given small volume of the atom is highest at the center, and decreases as one goes away from the nucleus, the number of these small volumes in each shell around the nucleus increases as the shell becomes larger.

Principles of Quantum Mechanics. The basic ideas of atomic structure were stated by Bohr some years ago and have been retained in essentially the same form in our present atomic theory. This theory has been of striking consequence in explaining a wide variety of experimental results. The various probability distributions that are possible correspond to different energy states of the electrons, and these energy-level designations are used to describe the electrons found in the various atomic shells. The innermost energy level is referred to as the K level, the next level as the L level, and so forth. These principal levels are further described as having various sublevels denoted by the letters s, p, d, or f.

One of the basic principles of quantum mechanics is that only specified energy levels are possible for electrons in atoms. These levels are numbered with the K level having the principal quantum number, designated $n = 1$, the L level having $n = 2$. A second principle is that the electron population of any energy level in an atom is limited to $2n^2$. This means that for the K level, the maximum number of electrons permitted is $2 (1)^2$ or 2; for the second level, the maximum number is $2 (2)^2$ or 8. Another postulation of the theory is that each main level of electrons may have a number of sublevels equal to its principal quantum number. This would give one sublevel to the K shell, two subshells to the L level, with the M level having three. Just as the number of electrons that can be put in any main shell is limited, so is the number of electrons in each subshell. An *s* subshell can hold two electrons, a *p* subshell six, a *d* subshell ten, and an *f* subshell fourteen. It is well known from chemical valence values that the outer shells do not contain more than eight electrons each.

The Periodic Table. From this kind of outline it is possible to describe all of the atoms of the elements of the periodic table. It might seem that each of the levels and sublevels should be filled in order, but this is not always the case. For example, it is found that the 4*s* level has lower energy than the 3*d* level. This means that, in some elements, electrons would be found in the 4*s* state before the 3*d* state is filled. Table 1.1 shows the electronic configurations of a few elements. The superscripts on the sublevel letters indicate the number of electrons in that particular subshell.

TABLE 1.1.   Electron Populations of Levels and Sublevels

Atomic Number	Element		Usual Chemical Valence
1	H	$1s^1$	1
2	He	$1s^2$	0
3	Li	$1s^2 2s^1$	1
4	Be	$1s^2 2s^2$	4
10	Ne	$1s^2 2s^2 2p^6$	0
11	Na	$1s^2 2s^2 2p^6 3s^1$	1
21	Sc	$1s^2 2s^2 2p^6 3s^2 3p^6 3d^1 4s^2$	3
57	La	$1s^2 2s^2 2p^6 3s^2 3p^6 3d^{10} 4s^2 4p^6 4d^{10} 5s^2 5p^6 5d^1 6s^2$	3

The information about these electronic configurations is obtained primarily from spectroscopic data in which the various spectral lines are considered as arising as a result of transitions of electrons from one energy level to another. Of course, the chemical behavior of the elements is determined by the

distribution of electrons in the atom with particular significance being attached to the number and arrangements of the
outermost or valence electrons. *One of the paradoxes involved in
the term "nuclear chemistry" is the lack of a relationship between the
nuclear properties of an atom and its chemical behavior.*

Electron Clouds and Energy Level Diagrams. It was pointed
out that we cannot describe the motions of the electrons in the
atom even though we can speak of their energy levels and can
give accurate descriptions of atoms by describing the number
of electrons in the various shells and subshells. Since we often
think in three dimensional analogies, let us suppose that an
atom were large enough to be seen and that a trail of smoke
were left by each electron in the atom. The density of the
smoke would tell us where the electrons had been, and from
this the probability of finding the various electrons at any
point in the atom could be determined. In Fig. 1.3a, the electron cloud is represented as a three-dimensional ball of smoke
with no well-determined pattern of motion or structure.

If, however, this electron cloud is cut in cross section (Fig.
1.3b), we should be able to see a series of regions in which the
electron cloud is more dense. Although this distinctness of
structure would indicate that the probability of finding the
electrons in certain regions of the atom is higher than finding them in other regions, there still would be no manifesta-
tion of precise motions. Even though the modern picture
does not describe the atom as containing electrons in "orbits,"
we can determine the location of the highest electron probability which does correspond to the radius of the orbit as described in the earlier static models of the atom. (For convenience, sometimes chemists still draw such plane orbits,
even though they visualize the electrons as occurring only in
clouds.) Our concern is, thus, not so much with the positions
of the electrons as with their energies. We may point out that

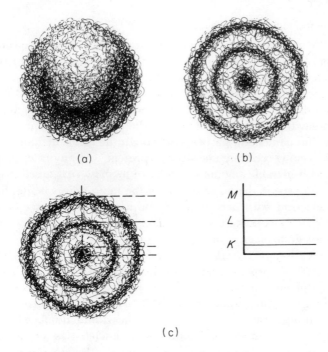

Fig. 1.3. Electron cloud density and energy levels for electrons in an atom.

an electron belonging to a given level of any atom may be found anywhere in space, but it does not use up its own energy in passing from one point to another so long as it is still associated with that atom. Hence, it is not necessary to draw circles to represent these electron energy levels. The same idea could be conveyed by drawing horizontal lines (Fig. 1.3c) to represent the electron levels. Such an "energy level diagram" is useful as a way of visualizing energy relationships, and is used extensively in modern descriptions of atomic and subatomic phenomena.

Composition of the Nucleus

We have mentioned the nucleus at several points. We commonly assign the location of the protons and neutrons to the nucleus. It was formerly thought that neutrons were composite particles made up of a proton and an electron, and it is unfortunate that some texts still give this implication. Present-day theories suggest that both the proton and the neutron are "fundamental" particles, although the exact definition of this term is certainly not clear at present. At any rate, there is a considerable amount of evidence to show that an electron cannot exist in the nucleus, one of the main points being that an electron must occupy a volume having a diameter of at least 10^{-8} centimeters for it to have the characteristics which we assign to an electron.

If we assume that the basic or fundamental particles in the nucleus are protons and neutrons, we may review the basic ideas of nuclear composition. For example, we know that hydrogen contains one proton in its nucleus, helium contains two, lithium three, and so on, with the atomic number being equal to the number of protons in the nucleus (as well as the number of electrons outside the nucleus). We are also familiar with the fact that hydrogen may exist in one of three forms called isotopes which differ in the number of neutrons in the nucleus along with the proton. Thus, hydrogen, with mass number 1, contains only the proton and is referred to as H^1. The hydrogen atom with mass 2 (H^2 or D) is called deuterium and contains a neutron and a proton. Similarly, hydrogen-3 (H^3 or T), called tritium, contains two neutrons along with the single proton. For convenience, we sometimes refer to the atomic number by the letter Z and to the mass number (the total number of particles in the nucleus) by the letter A. It can be seen that the nuclei of all of the elements can be characterized by the number of neutrons and protons present. The mass number is given as a superscript on the right in U.S.

usage, although most other countries place it on the left. Thus, the chemical behavior of the atom is related to the number of protons, but we find that all of the elements have isotopes characterized by differing numbers of neutrons. Incidentally, the term nuclide should properly be used to refer to any particular nucleus, and the term isotope retained for discussions of the various nuclear species of a given element. These terms are often used interchangeably.

One of the useful ways of presenting information relative to the various elements and their isotopes is to prepare a chart by plotting the atomic number against the number of neutrons for all of the known nuclei. Detailed charts are available, but, for our purpose, we can consider a highly condensed version of this graph, shown in Fig. 1.4. It is observed that at lower atomic numbers there is approximately a 1:1 correspondence between the numbers of neutrons and protons. As one proceeds to higher atomic numbers, there is a marked predominance of neutrons over protons. It is beyond the scope of this

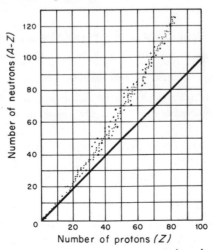

Fig. 1.4. Number of neutrons vs. number of protons for stable nuclei.

book to delve into the reasons for this, but one can observe what is sometimes called a "stability belt" corresponding to the neutron-proton ratios of the naturally-occurring nuclei. If one examines such a chart as this in more detail, one observes various generalities, such as the fact that odd-numbered elements do not have more than two stable isotopes, while even-numbered elements frequently have a larger number. Considerable effort has gone into the study of the relationships of nuclear composition and structure to nuclear stability.

Let us consider in more detail one of the problems involved in the build-up of various nuclei. The mass of a neutron has been found to be 1.008665 mass units, compared to the mass of a C^{12} nucleus which is assigned the mass value of 12.000000. (In 1961, the official reference standard of mass was changed from oxygen to C^{12}.) Similarly, the mass of a proton is found to be 1.007825 mass units on the same relative mass basis. According to the usual way of thinking, it is apparent that the mass of the H^2 nucleus consisting of a proton and a neutron should then be:

mass of neutron	1.008665 atomic mass units
mass of proton	1.007825 a.m.u.
mass of neutron and proton	2.016490 a.m.u.

One of the striking results of the determination of the various isotopic masses with precise mass spectrometers and other instruments was that the mass of deuterium (H^2) was not found to be the sum indicated above. Instead the isotopic mass of this nucleus was found to be 2.014102 a.m.u. This means that there is a difference in mass given by the following:

mass of neutron + proton	2.016490 a.m.u.
mass of deuterium nucleus	2.014102 a.m.u.
mass difference	0.002388 a.m.u.

This difference was formerly called the "mass defect," but this has given way to the term "binding energy" since a somewhat different concept is used for the explanation of this discrepancy.

Two of the oldest concepts of traditional science have been the two "laws" of conservation of mass and of energy. These were considered inviolate for many years, but were found to be inadequate shortly before Einstein developed his famous mass-energy equivalence relationship, $E = mc^2$, which relates the energy, E, to the mass, m, in terms of the velocity of light, c. He showed in his treatment of relativity that mass and energy are not two separately describable phenomena, but are identical, and that one can express quantities of mass and energy in the same or equivalent units. For example, we may calculate the energy equivalent of one gram of matter:

$$E \text{ (ergs)} = m \text{ (grams)} \times c^2 \text{ (cm/sec)}$$
$$E = 1 \times (3 \times 10^{10})^2$$
$$E = 9 \times 10^{20} \text{ ergs}$$

This energy is equivalent to 90 billion BTU (British Thermal Units) and is enough energy to heat an average home for 1000 years. It can also be shown that one atomic mass unit equals 931 million electron volts (Mev). It might be helpful to note that chemical bonds correspond to energies of a few electron volts and, thus, involve negligible mass equivalence. It may be pointed out that a correct reading of this mass-energy equivalence is not that mass and energy can be changed from one to the other but that they are the same. However, it is proper to speak of radiation being transformed into matter and vice versa.

In such a treatment, it is apparent that no discrepancy actually exists between the calculation of the sum of the masses of a neutron and proton and the deuteron which is the composite of the two. We think of the total reservoir of mass-energy as being constant, but the difference in the two masses is called the "binding energy" of the deuterium nucleus or deuteron. This is to say that

neutron mass + proton mass = deuteron mass + binding energy

One of the common units of energy in the nuclear field is the electron volt. This can be described kinetically as the energy possessed by an electron when it is accelerated across a potential of one volt, but the unit is used to describe all forms of energy and is not limited to kinetic energy. A commonly used multiple of the electron volt is the million electron volt (Mev) which is equivalent to 1.6×10^{-6} ergs, or about 3.8×10^{-14} calories. Ordinary chemical bonds have energies of about 3 or 4 electron volts. By using Einstein's equation given above and appropriate units for energy, mass, and the velocity of light, it can be shown that one atomic mass unit is equivalent to 931 Mev. The binding energy of the deuteron can thus be expressed either as 0.002391 atomic mass units or as 2.23 Mev. This is the energy which would be required to break the deuteron into its composite nucleons, i.e., the neutron and proton. We find that the same type of calculation can be carried out for any nucleus, and it is observed that, although the binding energy varies somewhat, there are certain regularities that are characteristic of this building-up process. The total binding energy of any nucleus is defined as the energy that would be required to separate the nucleus into isolated nucleons.

The total binding energy of an atom is equal to the difference between the isotopic mass of the atom and the sum of the masses of its neutrons, protons, and its extranuclear electrons. It is apparent that the total binding energy of a heavy nucleus is greater than that of a light nucleus, since it would have more nucleons to separate. However, it might be expected that the binding energy per nucleon should be about the same

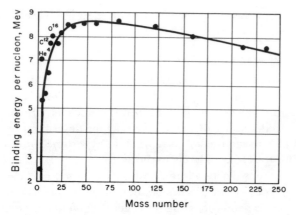

Fig. 1.5. Binding energy per nucleon for stable nuclei.

value. A plot of the binding energy per nucleon is shown in Fig. 1.5, which indicates that this quantity is relatively constant beyond the very light elements. From inspection of this curve, it can be seen that up to $Z = 56$, energy is released whenever nuclei are formed by the addition of particles. It can also be seen that for elements of atomic number greater than 56, energy would be required to add particles to the nucleus. This is to say that energy would be given off if such elements could be broken into smaller fragments. Chemists have used the terms exothermic and endothermic to describe reactions which give off or absorb energy, respectively, and we consider exothermic reactions as being those which will happen spontaneously (although we do not specify when such reactions will take place). The corresponding terms used for nuclear reactions are exoergic and endoergic, and we can thus say that reactions would be exoergic if they involve fusion of nuclei below atomic number 56 and if they involve fission above this atomic number. There is a wide region of atomic numbers near 56 in which the energy difference would not give rise to reactions involving high energy release in either direction.

The Structure of the Nucleus

We have considered the numbers and mass relationships of the nucleons in the nucleus, but nothing has been said about spatial and energy relationships in the nucleus. It might be useful to develop a diagram or model for describing these aspects of nuclear theory somewhat in the same way as was done for the electron levels in the atom.

Let us consider two large positively-charged particles. For the purposes of our discussion, one of these must be at least as large as a deuteron while the other particle must be at least as large as a proton. If these two large positively-charged particles are a great distance apart, they have a negligible effect on each other. Suppose, however, that one of them is moved toward the other. Since "like charges repel," a repulsive force (Fig. 1.6a) would be exhibited between them or, stated another way, work must be done on one of the particles to move it closer to the other. As these two particles are brought closer to each other, this repulsion, known as Coulombic repulsion, continues to increase until they are about 10^{-13} centimeters apart.

It may be surprising to learn, however, that if the particles are pushed still closer together, the repulsion abruptly decreases, becomes zero, and then becomes a "negative" repulsion at distances less than 10^{-13} cm. This, of course, would represent an attractive force between the particles and would be observed for the remainder of the distance separating them. We shall not discuss the nature of these strong, short-range, attractive forces here, but shall designate the region in which these forces operate as the nucleus of the atom. The nuclear radius is given by the following equation:

$$r = 1.4 \times A^{\frac{1}{3}} \times 10^{-13}$$

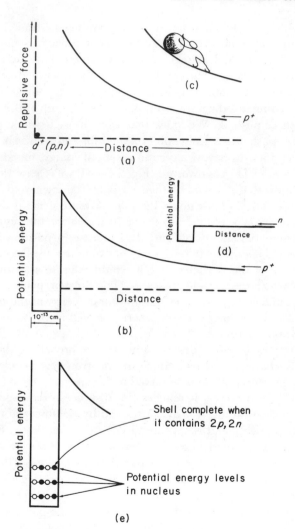

Fig. 1.6. Potential energy diagram for a nucleus.

in which r is the nuclear radius in centimeters, and A is the atomic mass number. The coulombic repulsion is not eliminated in this nuclear region, but the attractive nuclear forces are much greater. The continuation of the nuclear diagram is shown in Fig. 1.6b. It is interesting from the point of view of elucidating this diagram to think of it as a hill up which a ball might be pushed. We know that work must be done on the ball to push it to a given point on the hill, and we speak of the object, then, as having a certain potential energy, based on the gravitational forces involved (Fig. 1.6c). If we release the ball, we know that it would change its potential energy to kinetic energy and roll back down the hill. A more general description of this type of diagram is one in which the hill represents any potential energy system. In our case, a position on the potential energy scale represents not only the repulsion or attraction of the particles, but it would refer to the total energy which the particle possesses. The Einstein equivalence of mass and energy indicates that the total energy of the particle would include its own mass energy as well as the kinetic and potential energy.

Suppose we now consider a neutron approaching the positively-charged nucleus. Since the neutron has no electrical charge, no repulsion is observed as it comes closer to the nucleus. If, however, it reaches the distance corresponding to the nuclear radius, it is also attracted by the forces of the nuclear particles, and is captured by the nucleus (Fig. 1.6d). It should be pointed out that these nuclear forces arise from fundamental properties of the particles themselves. The property responsible for these nuclear forces among large particles such as protons and neutrons has been called the mesonic charge or more simply the "nuclearity" of the particle. Electrons are not found to have this property of nuclearity, and so cannot exist as a part of the nucleus. These forces are not thought of as being something external to the particles, as may be implied by the use of a term such as "nuclear glue."

We do not use such a "glue" concept in present-day theories.

Since protons and neutrons are the fundamental particles which can exist inside the nucleus, one very useful model suggests that these particles are arranged in shells or levels inside the nucleus in much the same way as the electron shells outside the nucleus. However, whereas the electron levels require different numbers of electrons to complete each shell, this model suggests that low nuclear shells are completed when each contains two protons and two neutrons. Combinations of various higher levels and sublevels are used for describing larger nuclei. Following the scheme described for electron levels, the nuclear shells can be represented by horizontal lines inside the nuclear region (Fig. 1.6e). These diagrams represent the *coulomb barrier* model or the *potential energy well* model of the nucleus in combination with a *shell* model.

Let us now consider an example of the way in which we can use this nuclear diagram by investigating a system consisting of a radon nucleus and a helium nucleus. The radon nucleus contains 86 protons and 136 neutrons, giving a total mass number of 222. The helium nucleus contains two protons and two neutrons and is identical to an alpha particle. We can calculate the energy required to push the helium nucleus to the edge of the radon nucleus. According to the equation given earlier, this radius would be about 9×10^{-13} cm. The energy of the helium nucleus at any distance from the radon nucleus can be calculated using the following equation:

$$E = \frac{q_1 q_2}{r}$$

in which E is the energy of repulsion, q_1 and q_2 are the charges on the particles, and r the distance separating the particles.

If such a calculation is made, the amount of energy needed can be expressed as approximately 27 million electron volts or 27 Mev. If sufficient energy were given to the alpha particle for it to overcome the nuclear potential barrier and combine with the radon nucleus, it would form a nucleus of radium with mass 226. We might point out that, according to traditional mechanics, the alpha particle should come back down the hill with the same energy required to push it up the potential barrier. To anticipate our further discussion, this actually is not the energy with which alpha particles are observed to be emitted.

A great many of the facets of nuclear theory are involved in experiments and calculations such as this. Much of our nuclear theory has been developed by means of experiments in which nuclei are bombarded with various particles at various energies and by determining the conditions under which the particles enter the nucleus or are scattered from it. There is no single generally accepted theory of nuclear structure and a great deal of effort and money are being devoted to experimental and theoretical approaches to this problem. The chemist is not ordinarily concerned with the details of nuclear theory except as it describes nuclear changes which give rise to different nuclei. One of the most important aspects of this field is based on the fact that many of the changes produced result in the formation of radioactive isotopes of the elements. Much of the remainder of this book will be devoted to a discussion of the radioactivity by which nuclear changes are detected and by which they are used in a great variety of applied problems.

It is, of course, true that a large amount of nuclear chemical tracer work is done with stable isotopes. In these experiments the isotopic ratio is determined with a mass spectrometer. If samples of various elements are enriched with respect to one of the isotopes, these mixtures can likewise be detected with mass spectrometers. Common enriched stable isotopes are H^2, O^{18}, and N^{15}. Since there are no suitable radioisotopes of oxygen and nitrogen, tracer studies with these materials give invaluable information about some very important chemical and biochemical systems.

chapter two

RADIOACTIVITY AND NUCLEAR REACTIONS

Natural Radioactive Series and Alpha Decay

Much of our interest in nuclear chemistry, as well as our knowledge of the nucleus, has been generated by work with naturally radioactive elements. Some forty species of nuclei with different radioactive properties have been identified as occurring in nature. By making physical or chemical separations when possible, by studying radioactive decay and growth curves as we shall describe later, by determining the specific properties of the emitted radiations, and in other ways, scientists have found that naturally occurring radioelements at the high atomic weight end of the periodic system fall into three distinct groups. These are known as the thorium series, the uranium series and the actinium series. In the first two of these, the series are named after the longest-lived members which start the series. The first member of the third series was thought originally to be actinium, but it has since been found to be one of the isotopes of uranium, U^{235}.

Since an alpha particle is identical to a helium nucleus, it has a mass of 4 and consists of 2 protons and 2 neutrons. Consequently, it is evident that in any disintegration in which an alpha particle is emitted, the atomic weight of the daughter element must be four units less than that of the parent. We

suggested that this alpha particle should come out of the nucleus with the same amount of energy (27 Mev) required to introduce it into the radon nucleus. One of the very surprising results in the early study of radioactive materials was that alpha particles come out of Ra^{226} nuclei with about 5 Mev rather than the 27 Mev expected.

The problem of how an alpha particle is able to come out of the nucleus with less energy than would be required to introduce it cannot be explained except by using a quantum mechanical way of describing the behavior of particles. This is difficult to comprehend in an ordinary sense, but it is the only method which gives an adequate description of the behavior of very small particles. Perhaps a reference to a fictional character, Mr. Tompkins, invented by Professor George Gamow, will help to clarify this point. In an interesting series of books, Mr. Tompkins had a group of surprising dreams about cars, tigers, baseball bats, etc. Since he could not understand the dreams, he went to the physics professor, who was able to interpret the dreams on the basis that the objects in his dreams behaved as if they were the size of subatomic particles. For example, Mr. Tompkins learned in one of his dreams that his automobile always possessed motion. (Note that this is not the same as saying that the car is *in* motion but, for the moment, we may think of it in the same way.)

In another episode, Mr. Tompkins dreamed that he drove his car into the garage, locked the door, and retired for the night. Imagine his surprise the next morning to find that his car was outside the garage (Fig. 2.2). Since this obviously could not happen, he asked the professor for an explanation and was informed that, as a matter of fact, it could happen. In quantum mechanics, he was told, if an object in motion strikes a barrier a sufficiently great number of times, there is a *finite probability* that the particle may pass through the barrier and appear on the other side. Actually, the mass of an auto-

Fig. 2.2. The quantum mechanical tunneling effect.

mobile is so great and its motion sufficiently small that we would not expect this to happen with actual automobiles and real garages. This, however, is the explanation for the emission of an alpha particle from a radioactive nucleus. We think of the alpha particle as striking the nuclear barrier a very great number of times, and find that occasionally the alpha particle appears outside the nucleus where it can be detected with suitable instruments. Since a given alpha particle may strike the barrier 10^{30} times before coming out, it is seen that this is a highly improbable occurrence, but methods of detecting these individual nuclear events are extremely sensitive.

As difficult as this idea might be to accept, the Gamow "tunneling effect" is our only explanation for alpha particle emission. The question might be asked, "Why do we accept explanations such as this for alpha emission and other experimental observations in the nuclear field?" The answer is twofold: (1) We have no other explanation based on our classical physical ideas and (2) the mathematical statements of these quantum mechanical concepts permit us to explain, verify, and to predict many new ideas about atomic and nuclear structure and relationships. For example, by using this method of description, we can explain not only the energy of the observed alpha ray emission, but also the probability of its occurrence, which gives rise to the experimentally observable disintegration rate or half life.

Nuclear Reactions

We have pointed out that alpha ray emission is a type of naturally occurring radioactivity characteristic of large nuclei. It is known, however, that radioactivity can be produced in all of the elements with suitable nuclear reactions. Let us return to our discussion of the introduction of particles into a nucleus, using the diagram of Fig. 1.6. We pointed out that a neutron required no energy to approach the nuclear "well," but that it was captured if it reached the nuclear radius. Since this type of reaction does not require the acceleration of a particle to overcome the potential barrier of the nucleus, it can be brought about very easily by placing a sample of a stable material (i.e., one containing one or more stable nuclides) in or near a source of neutrons such as a nuclear reactor or a neutron generator. Suppose we choose a sample of aluminum for irradiation with neutrons. By use of a mass spectrometer, it has been found that the only kind of aluminum found free in nature is Al^{27}. We may write the initial reaction between this nucleus and a neutron as follows:

$$Al^{27} + n^1 \longrightarrow [Al^{28}]^*$$

The Al^{28} first forms an excited or high-energy state, as denoted by the asterisk.

This reaction is diagrammed in Fig. 2.3. The Al^{27} nucleus (Fig. 2.3a) contains 13 protons and 14 neutrons and is described as being in a low level representing the stable nucleus. If a neutron is introduced, the total energy of the Al nucleus is increased to a much higher level (Fig. 2.3b).

This is the position which corresponds to the excited $[Al^{28}]^*$ referred to above. The question now arises as to how the excited $[Al^{28}]^*$ can give off its excess energy, and return to a lower state. This may happen in one of several ways.

The most probable process by which the excited $[Al^{28}]^*$ could lose energy would be to "cool down" by emitting the excess energy in the form of one or more "bundles" of electromagnetic radiation. These "bundles" are called photons of

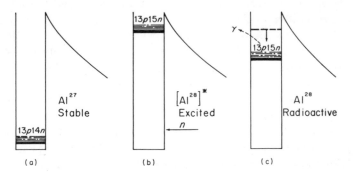

Fig. 2.3. Energy level diagram for neutron capture reaction.

gamma radiation. This emission would occur within a time interval usually of the order of 10^{-12} to 10^{-15} sec, and would leave an unexcited Al^{28} nucleus. This is usually the method of "choice." The energy level of the Al^{28} after the emission of gamma radiation is shown in Fig. 2.3c.

Another possible way for the excited nucleus to lessen its energy would be for a particle to "evaporate" from the excited nucleus. This would occur in essentially the same way that a molecule of water evaporates from a hot liquid surface—that is, one or more particles may obtain sufficient energy to overcome the nuclear "surface tension" leaving the nucleus with less energy. Several of these competing reaction possibilities are listed below:

$$Al^{27} + n^1 \rightarrow [Al^{28}]^* \begin{cases} Al^{28} + \gamma & (1) \\ Mg^{27} + p^1 & (2) \\ Na^{24} + \alpha^4 & (3) \\ Al^{26} + 2n^1 & (4) \end{cases}$$

Reaction (1) involves only the emission of gamma radiation, while the other reactions are concerned with the evaporation of nuclear particles. It is evident that if either reaction (2) or (3) occurs, a nuclear transmutation has taken place, giving rise to a different element.

One further point should be considered in this competition for energy release. Once the mass of the Al^{27} and of the neutron has been precisely ascertained, it follows that the mass of the excited $[Al^{28}]^*$ is the total of these masses. If, now, the mass of the less energetic Al^{28} is determined, we find that the Al^{28} has less mass than the total possessed by the nucleus in its excited state. The difference in mass between the reactant particles and the product nucleus—about 8 Mev in this case—is the total energy of the gamma rays given off. In reactions (2), (3), and (4) the masses of the product nuclei and the corresponding particles are greater than that of the excited [Al^{28}]*. This deficit indicates that these reactions will not occur unless additional mass (energy) is supplied. This can occur only if the kinetic energy of the neutron introduced is such that the total mass-energy available is at least as great as the mass-energy of the products. The energy which must be supplied in reactions (2), (3), and (4) is about 2.1, 2.7, and 11 Mev, respectively. Reaction (1) is seen to be exoergic, while the last three are said to be endoergic. A shorthand description of these reactions is often given as

$$Al^{27}(n,\gamma)Al^{28}, \quad Al^{27}(n,p)Mg^{27}, \quad etc.$$

The target nucleus is shown first, followed by the projectile particle and the ejected particles or radiation in parentheses, and finally the product nucleus is given. Another example of a nuclear reaction having special importance is illustrated by the following equation:

$$U^{235} + n^1 \rightarrow [U^{236}]^* \rightarrow Ba^{140} + Kr^{94} + \sim 2n^1$$

A great variety of fission product pairs are observed in fallout and wastes from nuclear reactors which use U^{235} as fuel. The example given is one of the most probable cases and occurs in about 5% of the fission events. Fig. 2.4 shows the fission yield curve for U^{235} fission. A specified fission reaction gives rise to a light and heavy fragment whose combined atomic number is 92. The mass numbers of the two fragments combine to give a value from 2 to 3 units less than 236, because of the neutrons emitted in the fission process. Pu^{239} and U^{233} are likewise fissionable with slow neutrons.

Beta Ray Decay

Upon examination of the nuclei of the elements in the region near aluminum, with a mass spectrometer, we find that whereas aluminum has only one stable nuclide (or nuclear

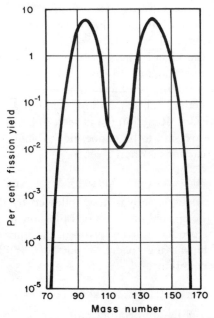

Fig. 2.4. Fission yield for slow neutron fission of U^{235}.

species), Al^{27}, the element magnesium has three stable isotopes, $Mg^{24, 25, 26}$. Similarly, Na^{23} is the only stable nucleus of sodium, while silicon has three stable isotopes. This information can be represented in a diagram as in Fig. 2.5, which is an expanded chart similar to a portion of Fig. 1.4. In Fig. 2.5, the atomic number is plotted against the mass number with the square blocks representing the stable nuclei. It has been previously shown that nuclei of Na^{24}, Mg^{27}, Al^{26}, and Al^{28} can be produced by suitable nuclear bombardments. Since these nuclei are not found free in nature, apparently each of these has excess energy still to be lost by some process before becoming stable. After its formation in the nuclear reaction, each of these could then be represented as an intermediate energy state as in the diagram Fig. 2.3c. These nuclei are shown as circles at their proper position in Fig. 2.5. Such atoms are said to be radioactive although in a different way than the alpha radioactive materials discussed above. Note that we have been describing only the nuclear states, but we assume that the appropriate numbers of electrons will always be associated with the newly-formed nuclei.

It can be seen that nuclei produced in nuclear reactions have either a larger or a smaller number of neutrons than the corresponding stable isotopes. Another way of referring to stability is to say that each element has a "preferred" neutron-proton ratio, or that the stable isotopes of the various elements cluster around a certain neutron-proton ratio. This stability ratio increases somewhat as one goes to higher atomic numbers, as shown in Fig. 1.4. Let us first consider what happens to those nuclei which have undergone a change such that the neutron-proton ratios are higher than for the stable isotopes of the element.

At first glance, it might seem that the easiest way in which a radioactive atom of this type could reach a more stable form would be by the emission of a neutron. This would result in the formation of the adjacent lighter nucleus of the same element. Actually, the extra neutron does not come out directly

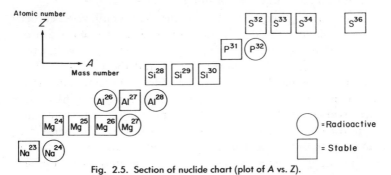

Fig. 2.5. Section of nuclide chart (plot of A vs. Z).

but, instead, undergoes a nuclear transformation into a proton and an electron. The proton remains in the nucleus, but, since the electron is not a component of the nucleus, it immediately leaves the atom. An electron formed in this kind of transformation is called a negative beta particle, and the process of disintegration is called negative beta decay.

To give an example of negative beta decay, let us consider the nucleus of P^{32} which can be formed either by the $P^{31}(n,\gamma)P^{32}$ or $S^{32}(n,p)P^{32}$ reaction. The nucleus of P^{32} thus contains 15 protons and 17 neutrons. Since the neutron-proton ratio is higher than that for stable P^{31}, the neutron transforms into a proton, which remains behind, and the electron, which is ejected from the nucleus. Since the resulting nucleus contains 16 neutrons and 16 protons, we recognize this to be a sulfur nucleus with mass 32. This transformation can be shown in the following equation:

$$P^{32} \rightarrow S^{32} + \beta^-$$

We determine, by referring to Fig. 2.5, that S^{32} is stable. To describe this transition in terms of an energy-level diagram, we may refer to Fig. 2.6. This shows the radioactive (or intermediate energy) level of P^{32} and reveals that the transition is not to a lower level of the phosphorus nucleus, but rather to the ground or stable level of sulfur.

Two other points should be made. We emphasized earlier that we do not consider the neutron to be composed of a proton and an electron. For this reason, we prefer to say that the neutron is *transformed* into the proton and the electron. (For example, we may say that a "2 x 4" block of wood came from the trunk of a certain tree. We do not say that the trunk of the tree is made of "2 by 4's".) The same matter is present, but a particle must have certain characteristics (e.g., dimension), in order to bear a particular name. This is also the case with many other nuclear particles, such as the mesons and other

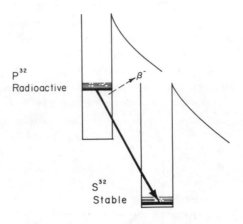

Fig. 2.6. Energy level diagram—negative beta decay.

"strange" particles. We do not necessarily visualize them as having a separate existence in the nucleus.

The other point that should be made for completeness involves the neutron transformation reaction itself. We have reason to believe that in addition to the beta particle, another particle is also ejected during the transformation of the neutron. This particle, which has quite interesting characteristics, is called the neutrino, ν (technically an antineutrino, although neutrino is frequently used in a generic sense). The complete neutron transformation would then be written

$$n^1 \longrightarrow p^1 + \beta^- + \nu$$

Gamma Emission

As was mentioned earlier, negative beta decay is observed when any nucleus has a neutron-proton ratio higher than that

possessed by its stable isotopes. Sometimes, however, the
nucleus still contains extra energy after the neutron transformation has taken place. For example, cobalt has a stable
nuclide of mass 59, which can be changed to Co^{60} by the addition of a neutron. It is observed, however, that when the Ni^{60}
is formed by the beta ray emission (Fig. 2.7), it is not in its
lowest possible energy state, even though the balance of neutrons and protons is a proper one for stable Ni^{60}.

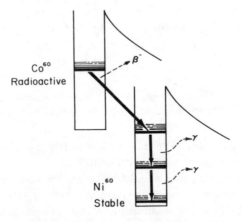

Fig. 2.7. Energy level diagram—negative beta
decay with gamma emission.

We referred earlier to a nucleus as cooling down in a manner similar to that observed for a liquid. We find here that
this energetic Ni^{60} nucleus may also give off its energy as
gamma radiation. In the nuclear reactions described above,
the gamma ray was given off immediately after the capture of
the incoming particle. In the β transformation described here,
the controlling rate is that of the beta ray emission. The
gamma radiation usually is emitted within a period of 10^{-12}

sec after the beta ray, although sometimes the gamma ray is delayed. It is important to realize that gamma radiation is always emitted as photons or "discrete" energy units. In the case of the gamma radiation following the decay of Co^{60}, the two gamma rays given off have energies corresponding to two different energy levels of the Ni^{60} nucleus.

Electron Capture and Positron Emission

The emission of a negative beta particle is essentially the only method by which nuclei with high neutron-proton ratios return to stability. It is evident that, if the radioactive nucleus has too few neutrons in comparison with the number of protons in the stable atoms of the element, it cannot reach stability by this process.

There are two ways by which a nucleus with a low neutron-proton ratio can reach stability. One of these is called electron capture. In this case, the nucleus with the high charge can trap an electron from one of the "orbital" or extranuclear electron levels, and can combine with it to form a neutron. A neutrino is also emitted.

$$p^1 + e^- \longrightarrow n^1 + \nu^0$$

Since the captured electron is usually from the innermost or K electron level, this process is sometimes referred to as K electron capture, or K capture, but the preferred term is simply electron capture. Although no radiation is given off in the primary process of electron capture, X-radiation is observed when an electron in a higher level falls into the vacancy to replace the captured electron. This process is represented diagrammatically in Fig. 2.8a in which the nucleus is shown to be at a higher level of energy since it contains an additional electron mass. The "daughter" nucleus may be stable, however (i.e., at the bottom of the well), if the resulting neutron-proton ratio corresponds to that of a stable nucleus. Any excess energy may be given off as gamma radiation following the electron capture process (Fig. 2.8b).

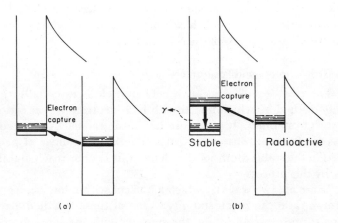

Fig. 2.8. Energy level diagram—electron capture.

One other reaction possibility exists for nuclei with low neutron-proton ratios to reach stability. This can take place whenever the final or ground state of the "daughter" nucleus is at least 1.02 Mev below the radioactive level. If this energy is available, it may be used to create a positive electron as in the following reaction:

$$p^1 + 1.02 \text{ Mev} \rightarrow n^1 + \beta^+ + \nu^0$$

The positron is a positive electron which, as in the case of the negative beta particle, cannot remain in the nucleus, and is ejected as a positive beta particle. This reaction competes with the electron capture process, if sufficient energy is available in the nucleus. Positron emission is shown diagrammatically in Fig. 2.9. Note that this emission may also be followed by gamma radiation if sufficient additional energy is present (Fig. 2.9b). The particular pattern that a radioactive nucleus

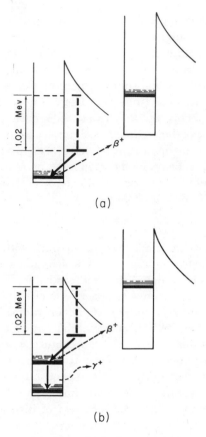

Fig. 2.9. Energy level diagram—(a) positron decay and (b) positron decay with gamma emission.

follows in becoming stable is called its decay or disintegration scheme.

A very interesting series of events sometimes occurs when nuclei are formed by the addition of particles to high atomic number elements such as uranium. If the resulting nucleus has a high neutron-proton ratio it will decay to the element having the next higher atomic number. The first of these synthetic transuranium elements was formed by the beta ray decay of an isotope of uranium (U^{239}, formed in neutron capture by U^{238}) to neptunium which then decayed to plutonium by another beta emission. There is good evidence that all of the elements up to element 103 have been formed, although some of their names have not yet been agreed upon. Most of the elements above 94 have been prepared by the bombardment of heavy elements in large particle accelerators. The nucleus of C^{12} has been used extensively as the projectile in these bombardments (Chapter 6).

The Curie

One of the basic units used in all work with radioactivity relates directly to the processes by which radioactive materials decay. It has been noted that radioactive materials "decay" when they change from a radioactive nucleus to another nucleus, which may be either stable or radioactive.   These processes always involve either alpha emission, negative or positive beta emission, or electron capture; gamma emission does not correspond to a nuclear transformation.   We may speak of the rate of decay of a radioactive material, then, in terms of disintegrations per unit time—typically, disintegrations per second. Since the numbers of disintegrations per second may become unwieldy, the term "curie" (along with its multiples and submultiples) has been introduced as a measure of the amount of radioactive material in a given sample. A curie of radioactive material was originally defined in terms of a certain weight of radium, but is now defined as a source which decays at the rate of 3.700×10^{10} disintegrations per second (dps). Similarly, a millicurie is a sample decaying at 3.700×10^7 dps, and a microcurie decays at the rate of 3.700×10^4 dps. Radioactive shipments are typically made in millicurie amounts for ordinary laboratory work, although sources of many thousands or millions of curies have been prepared for special purposes.

Radiation Background

One of the ever-present difficulties in the field of radiation measurements is the background of natural radiation which is always present. There are several sources of this radiation. The earth receives a more or less steady stream of cosmic radiations (each having 10^{10} to 10^{13} electron volts). This is usually observed as gamma radiation at the earth's surface. The variation of cosmic-ray background at various altitudes might be in the ratios of 1, 5, and 75 at altitudes of sea level, 15,000 feet and 55,000 feet respectively. At sea level, cosmic radiation intensity averages about 2 ion pairs/cm^3/sec which corresponds to 0.1 mr/day (Chapter 3).

In addition to cosmic radiation, other contributions are made to the background by the naturally radioactive radio-isotopes in the earth, air, water, and in the body. The largest amounts of radioactivity in the air arise from radon, thoron, and their daughters. These amount to about 10^{-10} microcurie per cm^3 of air. The decay products of these gases are solids and are brought down as a natural "fallout" by rain and temperature inversions. Drinking water contains traces of uranium, radium, and radon in concentrations of 10^{-9} to 10^{-10} microcurie per cm^3, although some spring waters contain 1000 times this concentration. Milk contains about 6×10^{-8} microcurie of K^{40} per cm^3. It might be interesting to note that the average human body is reported to contain an equilibrium concentration of about 190,000 disintegrations per minute of K^{40}, 150,000 disintegrations per minute of C^{14}, and 140 disintegrations per minute of radium. These disintegration rates correspond to the presence in the body of about 10^{20}, 10^{14}, and 10^{11} atoms of K^{40}, C^{14}, and Ra^{226} respectively. Fallout from nuclear tests has increased these radioactive levels by a few per cent.

INTERACTION OF RADIATION
WITH MATTER

Particulate Radiation

Gamma and X-radiation are found to be electromagnetic in nature. However, since alpha and beta radiations have measurable mass, they are referred to as particulate radiation. Alpha particles are emitted from nuclei with certain specific energies, with one energy value usually predominating (Fig. 3.1a). On the other hand, beta particles are ejected from a sample of radioactive material with a continuous distribution or spectrum of energies; that is, for a beta emitter one may observe all energies up to a maximum energy value which is then characteristic of that particular radioisotope (Fig. 3.1b). This maximum energy, E_{max}, is usually spoken of as "the" energy of a beta-emitting isotope, but one must remember that this only represents the energy value above which no particles are observed.

A useful, but not entirely accurate generalization is frequently made that the shape of all beta ray spectra are the same or that all such spectra exhibit the same distribution of energies below the maximum value. Spectrometers are used to determine the energy distribution and maximum values.

Since most laboratories do not possess spectrometers, one of the standard techniques employed to obtain useful information about the maximum values is to plot an "absorption"

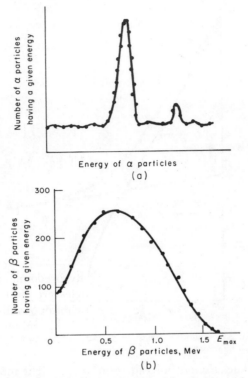

Fig. 3.1. Energy distribution of (a) alpha particles and (b) beta particles.

curve. If an alpha or beta ray source is positioned near a radiation detector, the sample will exhibit a certain counting rate (counts per minute). The placement of a thin foil of any suitable material such as aluminum between the sample and the detector will stop a certain fraction of the rays. If a thicker film is then interposed, a larger fraction of the radiation will be halted. If this process is continued with successively thicker films, a point is reached beyond which no appreciable change is observed. A constant value for the counting rate with the various foils may be caused by reaching the

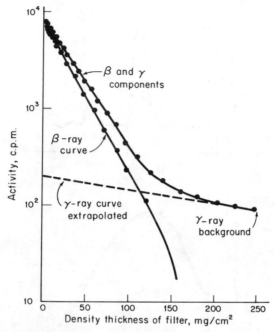

Fig. 3.2. Absorption curve for sample emitting beta and gamma radiation.

natural "background" of radiation, or it might indicate the emission of gamma radiation from the sample. Absorption-curve data are not precise, but valuable information about the energy of the radiation emitted from a sample can be obtained from such curves. An example of an absorption curve is shown in Fig. 3.2. This illustrates the presence of both beta and gamma radiation.

Another of the generalizations used in this field is that different kinds of material stop about the same amount of alpha and beta radiation, although it is evident that the amount of absorption depends on the mass of the material introduced into the radiation path. The determining factor in such absorption is the density of electrons in matter. It can be shown that the electron density of most materials is essentially constant. Since it is clear, however, that one would not expect a given thickness of aluminum to stop the same amount of radiation as the same thickness of lead, the density of the material must be considered.

Suppose that a particular source of radiation is shielded by 1 cm of a material having a density of 10 g/cm^3. If we now shield this same radiation source with a material whose density is only 1 g/cm^3, we could then determine the thickness of this latter material which would stop the same amount of radiation. If the kind of shielding is not important, it is apparent that 10 cm of the latter material would be required. It follows then that this relationship holds:

$$F = d x$$

in which F is the absorption factor, d is the density of the filter, and x is the thickness of the filter. In typical units

$$F = \frac{mg}{cm^3} \times cm = \frac{mg}{cm^2}$$

The absorption factor is thus proportional to the mass in a column of given area. This is the "density thickness" of the filter and is expressed in mg/cm^2 (or g/cm^2). Equal density thicknesses of various filters in mg/cm^2 thus give essentially equal absorption of the radiation. The data for absorption curves are usually plotted as the logarithm of the counting rate against the density thickness of the filters expressed in mg/cm^2.

The Interactions of Particulate Radiation with Matter

A consideration of the interaction of radiation with matter is of importance from two standpoints: (1) These interactions in a radiation detector permit us to detect and measure the radiations, and (2) this information permits us to shield ourselves from the radiation in order to work with radioactive

materials safely. Let us examine the nature of these interactions in some detail.

If we consider first an alpha particle passing through matter, our problem is to discover what happens when this particle comes near or "strikes" an atom. When the positively
charged alpha particle comes into the vicinity of an atom, it
interacts with the negatively-charged electrons of the atom. If
the alpha particle does not come too close to the electron, the
attraction may be such that the electron is only lifted from
one energy level to a higher one in the same atom. This process is called "excitation" (Fig. 3.3a). Since the electron cannot remain long in a higher energy state after the source of
excitation is removed, these electrons immediately return to
their lower levels, giving off their energy as X rays.

If the alpha particle approaches closer to the electron, or if
the electron is not held so tightly, it may be removed entirely

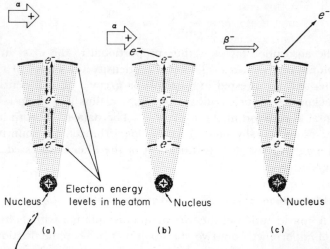

Fig. 3.3. Diagram showing interactions of particulate radiation with an
atom: (a) excitation, (b) ionization by alpha rays, and (c) ionization by
beta rays.

from the atom (Fig. 3.3b). The atom is thus separated into what is called an ion pair. The electron, of course, is the negative ion with the remainder of the atom being the positive ion. This ion pair may exist for a short period of time before the two parts are neutralized, either by recombination, or by being associated with and neutralized by other atomic components. In general, we assume that the alpha particle has sufficient velocity that it moves rapidly out of the field of the ion pair, and does not continue to have any effect on it after the ion pair's formation. We also assume that the alpha particle is so large that it follows essentially a straight-line motion, and is not deflected significantly from its path by production of ionization.

Although electrons may be either positive or negative, radioactive samples emitting negative particles are the more common of the two. When a negative beta particle passes near an atom, it also will interact with the electrons of the atom. In this case, however, the force is repulsive, and the electrons in the atom are repelled from the negative beta particle. As in the case of alpha radiation, this energy may be small enough to produce only excitation in the atom, or it may be large enough to remove the electron from the atom entirely with the formation of an ion pair (Fig. 3.3c). Positive electrons interact in essentially the same way by attracting the electrons from the atom to produce excitation or ion pairs.

But how much energy is involved in the production of an ion pair? The amount of energy required to remove an electron from an atom differs among atoms and for the diverse electron levels of the same atom. On the average, however, we find that it takes from 32 to 35 electron volts to produce an ion pair. This means that when a 1 Mev particle interacts with matter, it will continue in motion until it has produced

$$\frac{1,000,000}{35} = \sim 29,000 \text{ ion pairs}$$

before it will have lost all of its kinetic energy. Similarly, a 5 Mev particle must cause the production of about 140,000 ion pairs before coming to rest. When the particles do come to rest, they associate themselves with other atomic components to return to an electrically neutral state. The thickness of material required to permit the necessary ionization to use up the energy of alpha or beta radiation is called the range of the radiation.

Although the radiation particles require a certain number of interactions to give up their energy, it is found that the probability of the production of ionizations is not uniform along the path of the particle. It can be seen that a particle traveling at a slower velocity would have a higher probability of causing the formation of an ion pair than a faster particle, since it would spend more time in the vicinity of the atom. We may represent the change of ionization produced by a moving particle in Fig. 3.4. In this curve, the number of ion pairs formed per unit path length is plotted at various distances

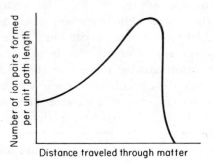

Fig. 3.4. Loss of energy by ionization as a particle passes through matter.

along the particle path. It is observed that for an alpha particle, the number of ion pairs formed per millimeter increases by several times as it slows down and approaches the end of its path. The ionization drops off rather abruptly after it reaches a maximum value. At the end of its path, the alpha particle associates itself with two electrons, and becomes a stable helium atom.

One other process by which high energy beta radiation gives up energy is called bremsstrahlung production. When a fast-moving electron changes its direction in the electrical field of the atom, some of its energy is given off as bremsstrahlung or "braking" radiation. This is electromagnetic radiation similar to X-radiation which is given off in a continuous spectrum of energies ranging from nearly the maximum energy of the beta radiation down to zero. This process accounts for only a few per cent of the energy loss from P^{32} beta radiation when absorbed in lead, and less for lower energy beta rays.

Electromagnetic Radiation

Electromagnetic radiation is usually thought of as wave motion, even though the energy is transferred as quanta of energy called photons. Such radiation is often characterized by its wavelength or frequency. The wavelength, of course, is the length of a complete cycle of the wave and for gamma rays may be of the order of 10^{-9} to 10^{-10} cm. The symbol λ is commonly used for the wavelength. The number of cycles passing a given point per second is referred to as the frequency and is usually denoted by the symbol ν. The frequency is related to the wavelength and the velocity of light, c, in the following way:

$$\nu = \frac{c}{\lambda}$$

The energy of the radiation is given by the following:

$$E = h\nu$$

in which h is Planck's constant (6.62×10^{-27} erg sec) and ν the frequency. Energy values may be expressed in ergs, Mev, or other suitable units.

As we have pointed out earlier, the primary interaction between alpha and beta radiation results in the formation of ion pairs, and these radiations are referred to as ionizing radiation. The nature of the interactions between photons and atoms is of a somewhat different type. Even though the end result is the production of ionization, electromagnetic radiation is referred to as nonionizing radiation.

Let us consider a hypothetical atom with electrons in several different energy levels (Fig. 3.5). There are two ways of describing the energy of these levels. One way is to refer to the amount of attraction between the electron and the nucleus

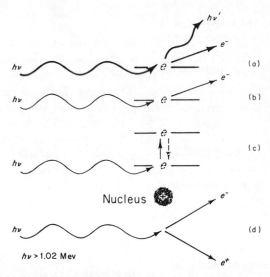

Fig. 3.5. Interactions of electromagnetic radiation with an atom: (a) Compton effect, (b) photoelectric effect, (c) excitation, and (d) pair production.

by considering the lower electron levels as being more tightly bound to the atom. From this point of view, inner levels may be considered to have lower energy states than those farther away from the nucleus. An equivalent way of indicating the energy scale, however, is to consider the amount of energy necessary to remove the electron from the atom by assuming that a free electron is the lowest energy state. From this point of view, less energy is required to remove the outer level electrons from an atom. For our purpose here, we shall consider the more tightly bound electrons as being in the lower energy state but more advanced work frequently uses the opposite convention.

Suppose a gamma ray of low energy (long wavelength) strikes an atom. If this energy is given to a low energy electron in the atom, it may be sufficient to raise the electron to a higher level in the same atom (Fig. 3.5c). (The alternative energy concept referred to above would suggest that while the low energy photon interacts with a high energy closely-held electron, the photon cannot remove the electron from the atom because of the high electron energy. The result is the same using either interpretation.) This is the excitation process mentioned earlier; this process would then be followed by the emission of X-ray photons characteristic of the difference in energy of the two levels involved. In this case, the total energy of the X rays given off is equal to the total energy of the incoming gamma rays.

We may now consider a somewhat higher energy gamma ray interacting with our hypothetical atom. If the energy is sufficiently great, the electron would be removed entirely from the atom (Fig. 3.5b). This is called the photoelectric process, and the electron ejected is referred to as a photoelectron. The kinetic energy of the electron, E_{e^-}, is equal to the gamma ray energy, $h\nu$, less the energy, W, needed to remove the electron from the atom, that is,

$$E_{e^-} = h\nu - W$$

Consequently, all of the photoelectrons formed by the inter-action of a gamma ray of a given energy with the electrons of a particular level would be ejected with the same energies.

Suppose now that a gamma ray having higher energy than the radiation giving rise to photoelectrons interacts with a very loosely bound electron (or a free electron) as shown in Fig. 3.5a. In this case, we have what is sometimes referred to as a "billiard-ball" type of collision, in which the energy of the incoming particle is distributed between the two "particles" in the system. Here the electron is set in motion by the inter-action with the radiation, but we observe that the electron takes away only part of the energy. The remainder of the en-ergy of the incoming gamma ray appears as a "scattered" lower energy photon or gamma ray. This process is called the Compton effect, and the secondary electron and the scattered gamma ray are called Compton electrons and Compton scat-tered photons respectively. The energy of the scattered gamma radiation and the electron in a given case will depend on the angle at which the electron and gamma may separate. It can be shown that there are certain limiting values for these energies, especially when scattering is at 90° and 180°.

The fourth possibility for interaction between a gamma ray and atom may occur if the energy of the incoming gamma ray is at least 1.02 Mev. In this case, the high energy gamma ray passing through the field of a nucleus may spontaneously transform into a negative and a positive electron (Fig. 3.5d). This process is called "pair production" and illustrates the transformation of radiation into matter according to the Einstein mass-energy equivalence relationship. The rest mass of each electron is approximately 0.51 Mev, so the initial en-ergy of the gamma ray must be at least twice this value for the two electrons to be formed. Any gamma ray energy in excess of 1.02 Mev is given to the two electrons as their kinetic energy.

In all of the cases described above, the secondary negative electrons set into motion lose their energy by the production of ionization upon passage through matter in exactly the same way as described for a beta ray. Consequently, the energy of the gamma radiation appears essentially as the production of ionization. The Compton photon undergoes other Compton or photoelectric collisions in which its energy appears finally as ionization.

There is, however, a difference in the final state of the positive electron formed in the pair production process. As long as the positive electron has kinetic energy, it loses it by the production of ionization in essentially the same way as for negative electrons except for its different charge. However, after coming to rest at the end of its path, the positron undergoes a final interaction with a negative electron. After combining for an instant, the pair of electrons annihilate themselves with the production of gamma radiation. In most cases, this gamma radiation consists of two photons, each having 0.51 Mev energy, and also being emitted at 180° to each other. These are called annihilation photons.

It must be understood that there are no specific ways to determine which of the various gamma-ray interaction processes would actually occur. While there is a general pattern for different energies as described before, each of the processes takes place only with a certain probability. When a gamma ray of a given energy interacts with a particular type of material, there may be a higher probability of one process taking place than the other, but we have no way of obtaining specific information as to which it will be. However, we can express this probability of occurrence as either the "absorption coefficient" or as a "cross section." These terms are both measures (expressed in different units) for the probability that a particular process will take place.

This probability can be visualized as the number of a certain type of interactions occurring in the passage of the radiation through a given amount (e.g., 1 cm) of the absorbing material. This "linear" absorption coefficient, the number of events per centimeter, is then expressed in cm^{-1} units. If the linear absorption coefficient is divided by the density of the material, we obtain the "mass" absorption coefficient which can be expressed in units of cm^2/g. As a typical example, let us consider the probabilities of the absorption of various energy gamma radiations in lead.

The probability for the photoelectric process is frequently symbolized by the Greek letter τ. A plot of this probability for different energies being absorbed in lead is shown by the dotted line in Fig. 3.6. It is noted that this probability decreases rapidly as the energy of the radiation increases. Although this curve is for lead, it might be pointed out that τ increases approximately as the fourth power of the atomic number, so lead would be a much better shield for radiation of this energy than would a lower atomic number material such as aluminum.

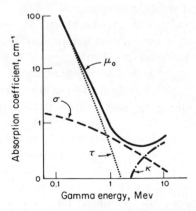

Fig. 3.6. Probability for electromagnetic radiation of various energies interacting by various processes with lead.

The probability for the Compton interaction is usually denoted by the symbol σ. This plot is shown for lead in the dashed curve in Fig. 3.6. There is not such a great change in this absorption coefficient with differing energies nor are there great differences observed with differing atomic number materials.

The probability of occurrence of the pair production process is represented by the symbol κ. This plot is represented as the dash-dot curve in Fig. 3.6. It will be noted that this curve begins at a point somewhat above 1.02 Mev and increases rather rapidly above this energy. This is a rather important mode of interaction for cosmic rays, but it is of less importance for radiation from radioactive substances.

The arithmetic addition of these three curves gives the composite or total absorption coefficient values for all of the different processes. This total, or measured absorption coefficient, is usually represented by the symbol μ_0.

$$\mu_0 = \tau + \sigma + \kappa$$

As an example, it can be seen from Fig. 3.6 that gamma rays of 0.2 Mev energy have a total probability of about 11 per cm. Of this value, there is about 90% probability that a photoelectric and about 10% probability that a Compton interaction will take place. Similarly for gamma rays of 1 Mev in lead, the absorption coefficient is about 1 per cm of which the relative probabilities for the two processes are about 30% and 70%.

While the absorption coefficient data represent the form in which this information is usually reported, it is helpful to translate this information into more practical units when considering the problem of radiation shielding. One of the characteristics of radiation having special importance for X- and γ radiation, is that it is absorbed in a logarithmic or exponential manner, that is, there is the same probability of stopping a given fraction of radiation by using the same thickness of shielding regardless of the initial radiation intensity. This relationship is mathematically analogous to the laws of radioactive decay that will be discussed in Chapter 5. From this concept one may derive the term half thickness, $X_{\frac{1}{2}}$, or the half value layer, HVL. This quantity, may be calculated from the total absorption coefficient, μ_0, by

$$X_{\frac{1}{2}} = \frac{0.693}{\mu_0}$$

Half-thickness values may be reported in units of cm or g/cm^2, depending on the units of the absorption coefficient used.

Half-thickness values for various energy gamma radiations are shown in Fig. 3.7. This curve is strictly valid only for well-collimated sources with well-defined geometrical conditions in which no scattered radiation contributes to the measurement. Consequently, it represents only an approximation to values which could be used in shielding workers from radiation in the laboratory. Typical curves from which half-thickness values can be obtained are shown in Fig. 3.8 in

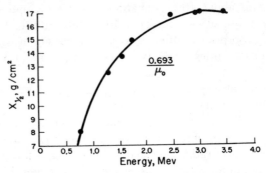

Fig. 3.7. Half thickness in lead for various gamma ray energies.

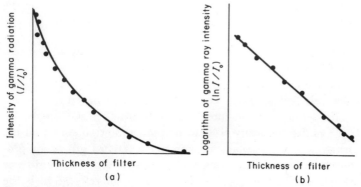

Fig. 3.8. Absorption curve for electromagnetic radiation in lead: (a) linear plot and (b) semilogarithmic plot.

which a linear and semilogarithmic plot of an absorption curve for gamma radiation are shown. These curves correspond to a particular kind (energy) of radiation and a particular type of absorbing filter. Gamma ray absorption measurements are usually made with lead filters to minimize scattering effects.

Radiation Dosage Units and Maximum Permissible Dose

It was pointed out in Chapter 2 that the curie is a unit for the measurement of radioactivity, that is, the measure of the disintegration rate of a sample. This gives only the rate of the emission of the various particles involved in the nuclear transformations. This unit gives no information as to the effect which the various radiations produce in matter, since the various types and energies of radiation may have widely different ionizing properties. Alpha radiation may produce perhaps 2500 ion pairs per centimeter in air; whereas beta radiation may give rise to 100 ion pairs per centimeter. On the other hand, gamma rays may have a specific ionization of only 1 ion pair per centimeter. Clearly, the total ionization which is the cause of the biological effects of such radiation interaction, is dependent both on the type of radiation and on the total number of radiation particles passing through the system.

In general, we can say that any effect of radiation is determined by the total amount of energy transferred to the system. Two units for expressing this energy are in common use, the roentgen and the rad. The roentgen, abbreviated r, was officially defined by the International Radiological Congress in 1937 as the "quantity of X- or gamma radiation such that the associated corpuscular emission per 0.001293 gm of air produces, in air, ions carrying 1 electrostatic unit of quantity or electricity of either sign." (The mass of air referred to is the weight of 1 cm³ of dry air at STP.) Perhaps, this definition may be clarified by referring to Fig. 3.9. This diagram illus-

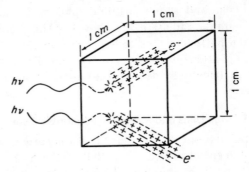

Fig. 3.9. Diagram illustrating definition of the roentgen unit.

trates that the definition is concerned with the effect produced in 1 cm³ of air by X- or gamma radiation. However, the "associated corpuscular emission," or the secondary electrons formed in the cm³ of air, may travel outside of this volume, and the resulting ionization must be included in the total ionization measurement. Furthermore, if the total ionization produced by all of these secondary electrons (when measuring either the positive ions or the negative ions) is equal to 1 esu of quantity of electricity, there is a radiation dosage of 1 roentgen. This corresponds to the dissipation of about 84 ergs per gm of air. The submultiple in common use is the milliroentgen, abbreviated mr.

Several limitations are imposed in this definition of a roentgen. One is that it is restricted to the measurement of X- or gamma radiation and another is that it is limited to a measurement in air. There is often a need for the measurement of the radiation effect in biological tissue, and it would be quite useful to have units which express the effects produced by other types of radiation. Another difficulty is that different types of radiations produce diverse biological effects, and many times the biological response varies also with the energy of the radiation. Several approaches to this problem of dosage units have been suggested, including the use of "roentgen equivalent" measurements (rep.—physical and rem.—mammal or man). Likewise, the term relative biological effectiveness (RBE) has been used extensively.

To avoid some of these complications, the International Commission on Radiation Protection adopted the "rad" unit in 1954. A rad is defined as the absorption of 100 ergs per gm of radiant energy. It is not directly related to the roentgen, but is roughly equivalent to the roentgen, since the energy absorbed per gm of tissue is about 93 ergs/roentgen. One advantage of this unit over the roentgen is that it is a direct measure of the energy absorbed by the system, so it can be determined directly by chemical or other types of dosimeters relying on energy absorption, and has a more direct relationship to the effect produced.

Although the rad has a number of advantages for theoretical work, the r, mr, rem, and mrem units are extensively used in practical discussions on radiological safety. The recommendations of the National Committee on Radiation Protection and the International Commission of Radiological Protection have been accepted by various government agencies and are in force at the present time. The requirements for the maximum permissible dose are based on the maximum one that a person may accumulate when working full time with radiation sources or radioactive material. This maximum permissible accumulated dose is given as 5 $(N-18)$ rem, in which N is the worker's age. This requires that no worker under 18 years of age be allowed to work professionally in a radiation area and that no person receive more than an average of 5 rem per year during his lifetime. Also, it is recommended that the rate calculations be made on a weekly basis, although the exposure interval may be increased to 13 weeks if the accumulated dose in the 13-week period does not exceed 3 rem. If one considers the average permissible rate during a year to be 5000 mrem, it is seen that the maximum rate during that year would then be approximately 100 mrem per week. The regulations, however, are not strictly applicable on such a weekly average, although this value may be used as an approximate upper limit.

It is known that other types of radiation have effects different from X, gamma, and beta rays for which the above limits are set. For example, thermal neutrons have a relative biological effectiveness of 2.5; fast neutrons, alpha particles, and protons have RBE values of 10; and heavy ions have RBE values of 20. The permitted dose for these radiations is proportionately reduced so that slow-neutron dosage would be limited to 40 mrem per week on the basis of the approximation above, while fast neutrons, alpha particles, and protons have limits of 10 mrem per week and heavy ion dosages are limited to 5 mrem per week.

It must be pointed out that the numbers quoted here and in other publications refer to the maximum *permissible* levels and are not considered radiation tolerances. No worker ever permits himself to receive any radiation unless it is necessary to perform a required operation. He is assured, however, that to the best of our scientific knowledge no ill effects will be suffered within these limits. In general, work with "generally licensed" quantities of radioisotopes do not entail significant radiation hazard. The field of health physics or radiological safety is one of the most important areas in the nuclear field, and is concerned with the problems of keeping radiation exposure to a minimum.

chapter four

THE DETECTION OF
NUCLEAR RADIATION

PART A. GAS DETECTION

Ion Collection Detectors

Since the interaction of the various types of radiation with matter results in ionization, the usual method of detecting radiation is by the collection of the electrons produced. The essential features of an ion-detection system are a pair of electrodes on which to collect the ions and a circuit through which the ionization current passes. Most frequently, these electrodes are arranged in a cylindrical fashion. A central wire is incorporated as the positive pole, the wire itself being surrounded by a conducting cylinder that acts as the negative pole. The electrodes are separated from one another by an efficient insulator and are usually connected to a voltage source that permits a potential difference to be applied to the electrodes as shown in Fig. 4.1.

Although ionization is produced when radiation passes through any kind of material, it can only be collected from a gas. The electrode cylinder may be filled with a gas, and a source of radiation brought into the vicinity so that the radiation passes through the gas so as to cause ionization in it. If, for example, the central wire is charged positively with respect

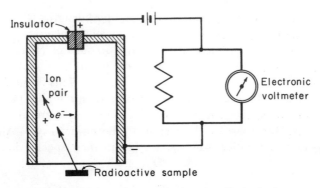

Fig. 4.1. Diagram of electrode system for detection of ionization in a gas.

to the outer electrode, the electrons produced will migrate to the central wire, changing its charge, while the positive ions will migrate much more slowly to the wall. Under suitable conditions, a current may pass from the central wire through the external circuit to the outer electrode. If this current can be detected, a measure of the radiation interacting with the gas in the detector can be obtained. The two general problems to be considered are those of determining the nature of the ion collection process in the detector tube and of detecting very small currents in the external circuit.

Electrode Voltage

To study the behavior of the ion-collection system, it is possible to describe in general terms what happens when the voltage in a hypothetical electrode system is changed and the manner in which the ion collection is dependent on this change. In a given detector, the charge collected after the passage of the radiation particles may vary because of the different numbers of ions formed by the particles as they travel through the gas in the collecting system. This may be the result of either a variation in the number of ions formed by the radiation or by a difference in the total path lengths which the particles traverse in the sensitive volume of the detector.

We may plot a curve showing the amount of charge collected per particle of radiation which enters the detector against the voltage on the electrode system. This is shown in Fig. 4.2. The results of the passage of an alpha particle through the detector is shown in the upper curve and the passage of a beta particle through it, in the lower curve. Alpha and beta rays differ from each other in their specific ioniza-

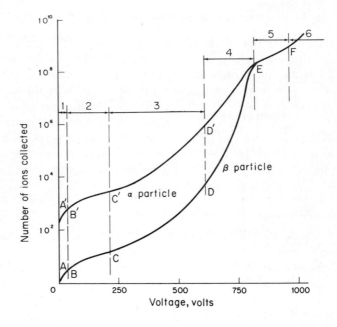

Fig. 4.2. Plot of the number of ion pairs produced for each radiation particle in a gas detector vs. the detector voltage. Regions: (1) recombination, (2) ionization chamber, (3) proportional counter, (4) limited proportionality, (5) Geiger-Müller, (6) discharge.

tion, that is, the number of ions produced per unit path length. This means that there might be many more ion pairs formed in the detector from the passage of one alpha particle than would be formed by the passage of a beta particle or an electron. The range of the beta particle may also be greater than the tube dimensions, which means that the electron may not expend all of its energy in the gas of the detector.

At low voltages, only a fraction of the number of ions formed in the detector may be collected because the weak electrostatic field allows some of the ions to recombine before they are collected. As the voltage increases, the field increases proportionately and all of the ions produced inside the detector are collected. This is shown by both curves when it is observed that they "level off" in the so-called ionization chamber region. Both curves level off, since the curves represent the collection of all of the ionization produced. This is called the region of saturation voltage, and is indicated by the segments BC for the beta radiation and $B'C'$ for the alpha radiation. For a typical ionization chamber of 250 ml volume, saturation is reached at about 10 volts.

In each curve, the saturation portion continues as the voltage is increased, as long as the "primary" ions are being collected. Primary ions are the ion pairs which are formed directly by interactions between the original radiation and the gas in the detector.

If the voltage is increased, a point is reached at which the primary ions are accelerated in the field of the detector to such an extent that they may also produce ionization. This is called secondary ionization. The result is that more ions reach the collecting electrode than were formed in the original collisions and the amount of charge collected per incident radiation particle increases beyond the saturation value. This process is called "gas amplification."

If the voltage is increased above this point, more and more

secondary ions are created, and the curve of charge collection rises rapidly with increasing voltage. The increase in the charge collected at the electrode is no longer independent of the applied voltage, as in the saturation region, but it increases rapidly with voltage. This region of voltage is referred to as the proportional region of ion collection, and is designated as CD and $C'D'$ in Fig. 4.2. It should be noted that the slope of the curve which corresponds to the rate at which the collected charge changes with increasing voltage is the same for both alpha and beta radiation. However, the number of ions collected will remain proportionately different in the two cases because of the difference in the specific ionization of the primary radiation. In this region the ion collection will be localized to a small portion of the detector tube.

It might appear that the amplification process could continue indefinitely as the electrode system is raised to ever-increasing voltages. However, another factor, the "space-charge" effect, becomes relatively more important at a higher voltage. You will recall that in the system described it was assumed that the central electrode was charged positively. Since the electrons are attracted to this electrode and have such small masses, they will be swept out of the detector gas very rapidly, leaving behind the positive ions. This positive ion region has the apparent effect of increasing the diameter of the central electrode which effectively reduces the electrostatic field intensity in the tube. This then is the "space-charge" effect. The result is that an upper limit of voltage is reached at which the number of ions that can be collected at the positive electrode is limited. This means that the multiplication of secondary ionization continues to increase, but much less rapidly than before.

This region in which there is not a strict proportionality between the radiation energy absorbed by the gas and the amount of charge collected is the region of limited proportionality, and is shown as the segment DE and $D'E$ in Fig. 4.2. In this region, the slopes of the curves for the alpha and beta radiation are not the same because of the greater effect of the high specific ionization in relation to the "space-charge" effect.

With a further increase in the voltage, one finds that the charge collected does not depend at all on the type of radiation or the number of primary ions initially formed. Instead, it is contingent only on the voltage applied to the electrode. In this region of operation, the field intensity around the central electrode is so high that any ion pairs formed, whether of primary or secondary origin, can be accelerated enough to cause additional ionization in the gas. A chain reaction is thus instituted and an "avalanche" of ions is created throughout the tube, and spreads along the central wire to envelop it with positive ions. In principle, any particle giving rise to a single ion pair in such a detector would be sufficient to cause the collection of the same number of ions at the electrode as a particle giving rise to many thousands of ion pairs initially. This region of voltage was first investigated by Geiger, and is called the "Geiger region" of ion collection. This is represented by the curve segment, EF, in Fig. 4.2.

If the voltage on the collecting electrode is increased even more, a limit is reached at which the tube discharges by giving multiple pulses and finally discharges in a "continuous" manner. In such an event, the counter will continue to count in the absence of external radiation. Operating the counter at such voltages can damage the detector tube.

Common Laboratory Instruments

There are three standard types of detectors based on ionization collection in gases. Those that operate in the region in which the voltage is insufficient to cause gas amplification are known as ionization chambers. The most common of these are gold-leaf and gold-plated quartz fiber electroscopes such as the Lauritsen or Landsverk electroscopes. Direct-reading pocket dosimeters used for personnel monitoring are likewise of this type.

To illustrate the magnitude of the ionization current, consider an instrument with a typical charging voltage of a few hundred volts. The electrons might drift at the rate of about 10^5 cm/sec, while the positive ions would move about 100 cm/sec. Since the electronic charge is 1.60×10^{-19} coulomb, the current produced in such an ionization chamber might be of the order of 10^{-17} amp. It is not possible to measure such a small current with a galvanometer, so other methods of current detection must be employed as will be described below.

The primary construction difference between an ionization chamber and a detector operating in either the proportional region or the Geiger region is the fact that much larger center wires are used in ionization chambers. The smaller wire in the Geiger and proportional counters produces a higher voltage gradient in the vicinity of the wire. In principle, a detector may function either as a proportional counter or as a Geiger-Müller counter, but in practice the filling gas and voltage ranges are selected for optimum operation in only one of the regions. Typical filling gases for proportional counters are methane, carbon dioxide, or a commercial mixture of argon and methane. Proportional counters frequently operate at atmospheric pressure.

The voltage necessary to operate in the proportional region increases with higher gas pressure and with a higher ionization potential of the gas used. The operating voltages are usually between 1000 and 5000 volts. The system usually requires an external amplifying circuit to obtain pulses that can be measured satisfactorily.

Detectors operating in the Geiger region (Geiger-Müller or G-M counters) have sufficiently high voltage across the electrodes that gas amplification in the detector is of the order of 10^7. This means that 10^7 ions are collected at the electrode for each primary ion pair formed. Under these conditions the discharge covers the entire length of the central wire, and all of the current pulses are of the same size or have the same "pulse height." Since G-M counters frequently operate at low pressures, typical operating voltages are in the range of 1000 to 2000 volts, although some types of filling gas mixtures may permit operation at much lower voltage. The gas fillings for G-M counters are usually mixtures of an inert gas (such as neon or argon) and either an organic compound (such as ethanol) or a halogen gas (such as chlorine or bromine).

One of the problems inherent in G-M counting is that the positive ion "sheath" moves so slowly toward the walls of the detector that the tube is inoperative for a long time between successive pulses (see discussion of resolving time below). Another related difficulty is that the heavy positive ions may be sufficiently accelerated when they strike their collecting electrode that electrons may be knocked out of the electrode by the collision. These electrons would trigger the detector again unless some means of stopping the discharge for a short period of time were used. Some of the early workers employed electronic circuits to lower the voltage for a very short period of time during the period of positive ion collection. More recently, the standard procedure has been to introduce an organic "quenching" gas. These polyatomic molecules dissociate in absorbing the energy from the ions, or distribute the energy among the bonds in the molecule so that the velocity of the molecule is not high enough to knock out secondary electrons on impact with the electrode. Since the organic molecules are disrupted in the process, there is a finite lifetime for detectors employing this type of quenching. A relatively recent development is the use of "halogen-quenched" tubes in which the halogen molecules recombine after the quenching process. This type of tube thus has an "infinite" life, and is excellent for many purposes, although it has some disadvantages for certain laboratory uses, particularly when employed with poorly regulated high voltage supplies.

Current Measurement

Now that we have discussed the general mechanism of a gas-detection system, we will consider techniques by which the ionization current may be measured to give information on the radiation intensity from a given sample or in a given region near a source. This may be done in one of two ways. We may either (1) determine the total number of ions collected, which would give us the total amount of ionization produced (cumulative instruments) or (2) measure the number of radiation pulses caused by the ionization entering the detector (pulse counters). An example of no. (1) is the gold-plated fiber instrument (dosimeter) in which the accumulated deflection of the fiber is proportional to the total number of ions collected. However, the same total measurement would be obtained either by the collection of the ionization for a relatively few alpha particles or from a large number of beta particles.

The rate of radiation emission is, perhaps, more frequently desired in the laboratory than the total amount of ionization. To determine this rate, one of two general methods is employed. In the first one, the actual rate of the charging or discharging of an electrical capacitance is used. This may be observed directly as in the determination of the rate of discharge of a gold-fiber electroscope with a timer, or indirectly by the use of an electronic circuit called an electrometer. The rate of drift of the leaf or of the electrometer needle is used as a measure of the rate of charge collection, and is thus a measure of the rate at which radiation is entering the detector.

In addition to the "rate of drift" determination a second general method of current measurement involves the use of Ohm's law more directly. This may be stated in the following equation:

$$V = I \times R$$

in which V is the voltage produced by a current I passing through a resistance R. The ionization current may be passed directly through a resistor as the corresponding voltage drop across the resistor is measured. The amount of the deflection of the voltmeter is then proportional to the rate of ionization collection. This reading would vary if the rate at which the radiation passed through the detector changed. Readings would also differ upon the entrance of given number of particles of diverse types of radiations.

Pulse Counters

The foregoing discussion considered what may be called cumulative or average radiation level instruments. These are instruments utilizing the total effect of the radiation in the detector either in determining the total ionization obtained or the rate of ionization production. If, on the other hand, it is desirable to know only the number of radiation particles entering the detector in a given period of time and not necessarily their ionizing effectiveness, it is possible to use what might be called a "pulse" counter.

The detector may be any of the types of detectors described above (or a scintillation detector as described in Part B of this chapter). One component that most electronic radiation detectors require is a high voltage supply designed for voltages from 500 to 5000 volts or higher.

Since any electrical circuit has small random "noise" signals, it is apparent that some differentiation between the pulses from the radiation source and the random noise pulses is necessary. Actually, the basic differences between a pulse counter and a cumulative instrument involves a distinction between the lengths of time during which they permit the ionization to be collected in the detector. This is determined by the design of the electronic measurement circuit. Cumulative instruments use long collection times, while pulse counters permit the ionization to be collected in very short periods.

All pulses attain some maximum amplitude, depending on the number of ions produced and the type of circuit used. The pulse is shown as a negative pulse in Fig. 4.3, since it is the electron collection which is of primary interest. This maximum amplitude of the pulse is referred to as the "pulse height." A discriminator is a component of the electronic circuit that blocks or discards all pulses below some predetermined amplitude. Such circuits are a part of all pulse-registering devices and, in principle, allow one to record radiation pulses and reject noise pulses. The pulse amplitude barely required to pass the discriminator is called the "input sensitivity" of the circuit.

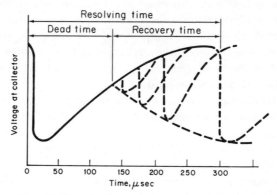

Fig. 4.3. Plot of collector voltage vs. time in a gas detector system.

From the discussion regarding gas detectors above, it can be seen that if a second radiation particle enters the detector when the tube is being swept free of its ion pairs, the detector could not give another pulse as large as the first, since the electrostatic field in the detector would be insufficient for the production of the required amount of ionization. The detector has a certain "dead time," i.e., a period during which no pulses are formed. While the positive ions are being cleared from the detector, there is a period called the "recovery time" during which the field again builds up to give pulse heights equal to the maximum value. This means that with a given discriminator setting or input sensitivity in a measuring circuit, the pulses would not be accepted by the circuit until they had reached a certain height.

Any combination of a detector with its associated amplifying and recording circuit has what is known as a "resolving time." This is the period of time between the passage of one pulse in the circuit and the recovery of the circuit to such a point that another pulse can be accepted. During this period, the counter will not be able to separate and measure closely spaced impulses. The resolving time is determined by the geometrical design of the detector and the resistance and capacitance characteristics of the electronic circuit. Typical values for a proportional counter may be from 1 to 10 microseconds, while G-M counters commonly have resolving times of 200 to 300 microseconds.

Although a G-M counter may produce a sufficiently large pulse to be registered directly, the other types of ion-collection and scintillation systems do not. For these instruments, it is necessary to amplify the pulses in one or more steps.

Much of the early work was performed by attempting to count the individual current pulses on a pulse-registering device such as a mechanical counter, but a major advance was made with the introduction of a "scaling" circuit. This was a device which would divide the number of pulses recorded by the mechanical register by a scaling factor such as 8, 64, or some other power of 2. More recently, instruments have been made using decimal scaling components. This shows the number of pulses registered directly in powers of 10. It is also possible to employ an instrument which electronically determines the rate at which the pulses are given out by the detector. Such an instrument, called a "counting rate meter," is particularly valuable when instantaneous counting-rate information is needed directly as with instruments involving a recording chart or medical scanning techniques.

While it is theoretically possible to consider a counter which would operate in either a proportional or Geiger region, in practice only one of these regions is used. Since much routine work is carried out with G-M counters, we might consider a rather special characteristic of these instruments. Because of the electronic limitations in a circuit accepting pulses from a counter, there is a voltage minimum below which no pulses would be accepted by the electronic amplifying and recording circuit. The voltage necessary to obtain a large enough pulse to record the impulse in the circuit is called the threshold voltage, and is a characteristic of a particular detector tube and circuit. The first step in operating a counter, then, is to determine this threshold voltage by bringing a radioactive

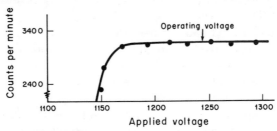

Fig. 4.4. Counting rate at various voltage settings for a G-M counter exhibiting a "plateau."

sample into the vicinity of the detector and then turning the voltage up until the impulses start registering in the counter (Fig. 4.4). The advantage of this plateau in a Geiger-Müller counter is that the sensitivity of the instrument is relatively independent of small changes in the high voltage across the detector electrodes.

PART B. SCINTILLATION DETECTION

The Scintillation Process

The scintillation counter has been employed extensively during the last several years and differs somewhat in principle from the ion collection detector. Since much of the usefulness of these detectors arises from their high efficiency for gamma detection, let us review briefly the gamma interaction mechanisms.

It was pointed out that several possible types of interaction may occur between gamma radiation and matter, including the photoelectric, Compton, and the pair-production processes. It was also mentioned that in the photoelectric process a large fraction of the energy of the gamma ray photon is transferred to an atom in the absorbing material, which then ejects an electron from it. Similarly, in the pair-production process, the gamma ray energy goes into the formation of a pair of electrons, each with a certain amount of kinetic energy. In the Compton process, only part of the energy of the photon is transferred to the electron, since a scattered photon of lower energy is also produced. One or more electrons is set in motion in each of these types of processes.

These electrons, as well as those given off in alpha and beta interactions, lose energy when passing through matter either by the ionization or excitation of the atoms through which they pass. There are a number of substances such as ZnS that absorb such ionization and excitation energy and re-emit a certain fraction of it in the form of violet or ultraviolet light. These materials are frequently called phosphors. The violet light wavelength corresponds to an energy of about 3 electron volts.

If one assumes that all of the electronic energy is used up within the scintillating material, the number of photons of visible light produced is proportional to the energy of the electron absorbed. For example, suppose that an electron has 1 Mev energy or is given 1 Mev of kinetic energy by a gamma ray interaction. If 5% of this energy is transferred to visible light, this would produce about 17,000 "blue" (3 e.v.) photons. It is the process of detecting these photons that is the basis of the scintillation detector. It is difficult to detect the flash of visible light from such a number of photons by visual means, and this method of radiation detection was not highly developed until the perfection of the photomultiplier tube. This tube is a device that converts the light flashes to photoelectrons, and multiplies the number of electrons to give a measurable pulse. The height of each pulse is then proportional to the energy absorbed by the phosphor.

In the scintillation detection of gamma radiation, the energy absorption by the phosphor is seen to correspond to a certain proportion of the energy of the original gamma ray, depending on the type of gamma ray interactions which took place. The number of photons produced in the phosphor is proportional to the total energy observed. If the original interaction was a photoelectric effect, all of the incident energy is absorbed. If the interaction was by a Compton process, the number of photons would represent only the energy of the Compton scattered photon (unless the photon was scattered back into the detector). The light produced in this interaction would thus represent less energy than that of the original gamma ray. It might be pointed out, however, that larger volumes of scintillating material would increase the probability of capturing the secondary Compton gamma radiation.

The two general types of phosphors are solids, which may be either inorganic or organic materials, and liquids. Sodium iodide crystals with a slight trace of thallium as an activator, NaI(Tl), have high efficiency for gamma ray measurement, since they have a high density (3.67 g/cm^3) and a high atomic number (53 for iodine). Anthracene, stilbene, and special plastics have special advantages for certain problems of alpha and beta measurement.

One disadvantage of NaI(Tl) crystals is that they are hygroscopic and must be encased in a watertight container. These crystals may be purchased either canned or uncanned and either as solid crystals or as "well"-type crystals. The latter have holes drilled part of the way into the crystal in which the sample can be placed for higher geometrical efficiency.

One of the most rapidly developing areas in applied nuclear chemistry is that of the use of liquid scintillation counters. These systems are of particular interest in the detection of low energy or "soft" beta radiation or in other situations which require high geometrical efficiency and minimal self-absorption corrections. Liquid scintillation detection is often the best method for the measurement of tritium, carbon-14, or sulfur-35, and it has been used extensively within the last few years in biological and biochemical work. For such scintillation systems, it is necessary to employ some combination of solvent and a liquid scintillator compound. A typical combination is a solution of diphenyloxazole in toluene. Since some of these scintillator materials do not fluoresce in the visible region, it is sometimes necessary to include in the solution another compound that can absorb the ultraviolet excitation energy and re-emit it at a wavelength that can be detected in the phototube. Plastic scintillators contain the scintillating compound dissolved in a solid plastic material.

Since the pulses from weak beta emitters in liquid scintillation systems are very small, it is frequently desirable to place the detector solution and the photomultiplier in a deep freeze unit to minimize the random electronic pulses of "noise" in the photomultiplier. The number of background pulses is considerably diminished if this procedure is followed.

The Photomultiplier Tube

The next step in the detection of radiation in a scintillation system is to transform the light energy into an electronic signal of sufficient strength that it can be measured in standard counters. This is done by the introduction of a photomultiplier tube. A schematic diagram of such a tube is shown in Fig. 4.5. The photocathode is frequently made of a cesium-

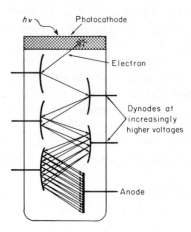

Fig. 4.5. Schematic diagram of photo-multiplier tube.

antimony alloy. When the light passes through such a photo-cathode, a 3 e.v. photoelectron may be ejected with approximately 5 to 10% efficiency, that is, there will be one photo-electron ejected into the photomultiplier tube for every 10 to 20 photons in the phosphor which impinge on the photo-cathode of the photomultiplier.

After the emission of the photoelectrons into the tube, the photoelectric current is then amplified. This is done by focus-ing the photoelectrons on the first of a series of dynodes. These are electrodes so arranged that the electrons from each preceding stage are focused on the next. Each dynode in the series is at a potential higher than that of the preceding one. The difference might be of the order of 100 volts for each dynode in a typical tube. The increase in voltage on the suc-cessive dynodes causes the production of additional secondary electrons at the next dynode surface. Since the tube is evacu-ated, there is no absorption of electrons and a large amplifica-tion factor is attained within the tube. For example, if the voltage across each dynode in the tube is sufficient to cause the appearance of two secondary electrons for each incident electron per stage and if one assumes 100% efficiency in the focusing at each stage, a tube with 10 dynodes would have an over-all amplification factor of 2^{10} or 1024. Commercial tubes have 6 to 14 dynodes with secondary emission ranging from 3 to 5 electrons per stage.

Integral Scintillation Instruments

It is evident that the scintillation detection system is quite applicable to straightforward radiation counting, that is, it may be arranged to give a counting rate directly proportional to the number of the pulses produced in the phosphor. Instru-ments such as this would be quite suitable for "relative" counting, which is the technique used by most workers with radioactive tracers. Although a scintillation counter will count only a certain fraction of the gamma rays originally incident on the phosphor, the counting rate for two samples of the same radioisotope would be proportional to the disintegration rate of the radioactive material in the two samples. Samples of radioisotopes may be placed near the scintillation crystal in some easily reproducible position or inserted in a suitable holder into a hole or "well" in the crystal. It should be pointed out that the efficiency of a crystal decreases when some of the crystal is removed to form the well. However, this factor may be partially overcome by the increased solid angle available for detection by placing the sample inside the crystal. This instrument is particularly useful for measuring liquid samples which may be placed in test tubes or other holders for insertion into the well.

Energy-Differentiating Scintillation Systems (Pulse Height Analyzers)

In any type of proportional counting (either a proportional ion collector or a scintillation detector), it is frequently desirable to know the number of pulses that have a pulse height exceeding some variable setting of the discriminator (see Part A) or pulse height selector (PHS), that is, it is desirable to know the number of pulses in a measurement that are in excess of the selected setting of the PHS. With some instruments, this is possible by setting the PHS at a given point and varying the detector voltage. However, for precision measurements it is more desirable to have an accurate control on the PHS which allows a variation in the size of the pulse to be accepted. Such a discriminator setting is frequently expressed in volts.

In a scintillation measurement, we sometimes need to know the number of pulses with certain heights. This number would, of course, correspond to the variation or the spectrum of energies of the rays absorbed in the phosphor. An instrument called a pulse height analyzer is usually employed to determine the energy distribution of pulses being received by an instrument. This is a circuit composed of two discriminator units and a special circuit that permits or prevents, in some cases, the registry of two or more events occurring within a certain time limit (Fig. 4.6).

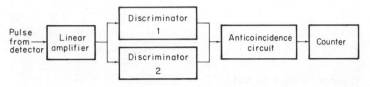

Fig. 4.6. Schematic diagram of pulse height analyzer circuit.

The pulse height analyzer is analagous to a pathway in which two gates are placed. The first gate is kept closed while the second one is normally open. If an object strikes the first gate, it opens to let the object pass. On the other hand, if the object passes through the second one, this gate automatically closes. The objects of special interest in our case, are those which stop in the space between the two gates. These can be identified because both gates are open during the time of passing—the first because the object made its way through it, and the second because the object did not pass that far. The "objects" of interest in the pulse height analyzer are pulses that have sufficient energy to pass through the lower discriminator (D1), but do not have enough energy to pass through discriminator (D2) with the higher setting. The pulses to be registered are those which lie between some predetermined lower pulse height or energy value and the upper pulse height setting.

With this type of instrument, it can be seen that only pulses occurring within some selected difference of pulse heights are allowed to pass to the register. The voltage separation between the two discriminators is frequently called the "window" width. An instrument consisting of a pair of discriminators and its anticoincidence circuit is called a single-channel analyzer. More complex instruments are capable of simultaneously recording the number of pulses occurring in several channels or window settings. Commercial instruments operating with 256 or more channels are now available. The study of the decay times and energies of short-lived isotopes is greatly facilitated by the use of such multichannel analyzers.

Gamma Ray Spectrometry

The information from a pulse height analyzer is usually plotted with the number of pulses or counts at each pulse height setting of the instrument. Since the pulse height setting corresponds to a given value for the energy absorbed in the phosphor, this value corresponds to the energy of the radiation. A curve showing the number of counts at each energy for a sample of Cs^{137} is shown in Fig. 4.7.

It can be seen from the curve that there is a "photopeak" at energy of 0.661 Mev. This corresponds to the total energy absorption of the radiation interacting with the crystal. The Compton interactions give rise to electrons having less than the maximum energy, which is shown on the curve as a "plateau" region at energy values less than that of the photopeak. Other characteristics of the spectrum are indicated in the figure. If there were several gamma rays coming from the sample, a corresponding number of photopeaks and overlapping Compton regions would be observed. With suitable instruments it is possible to study specific gamma rays arising from a particular isotope in the presence of a wide variety of other radiations.

Solid State Detectors

An interesting recent development in the instrumentation field has been the introduction of solid state radiation de-

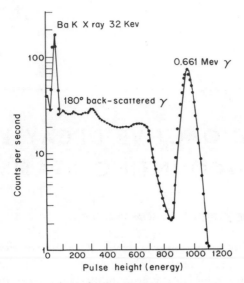

Fig. 4.7. Gamma ray spectrum of cesium-137.

tectors. These are radiation detectors primarily used for the detection and energy measurement of heavy particles such as alpha particles, protons, and fission fragments.

Mass Spectrometers

Little has been said of the detection and measurement of stable isotopes of value in various types of tracer experiments. Mass ratios of various isotope mixtures can be determined with a mass spectrometer which usually operates on the principle that differing radii of curvature in a magnetic field are observed for particles having differing masses.

chapter five

RADIOACTIVE DECAY LAWS
AND COUNTING STATISTICS

PART A. THE RATES OF RADIOACTIVE DECAY

One of the most important characteristics of radioactivity is the "regularity" of the disintegration process, based as it is on a purely random decay probability. This is the more striking, since we have no information on the dynamics of the decay processes of individual atoms. We use the decay laws solely on the basis of the generalization that there is a regularity in the number of atoms decaying per unit time—but only when there are a statistically large number of radioactive atoms in the sample. *These laws, which give rise to such concepts as half life, average life, etc., are entirely statistical in nature and are valid only when large numbers of radioactive atoms are under consideration.*

Fundamentals

The basic laws of radioactive decay were studied extensively by many workers in the early days of nuclear chemistry. It was found experimentally that for a single pure substance the rate of change in its radiation emission rate with time was proportional to the number of radioactive atoms in the sample. This can be expressed in the notation of the calculus

$$\frac{dN}{dt} \propto N \tag{1}$$

in which N is the number of radioactive atoms in the sample, dN is the change in the number of atoms, and dt is the change in time. By introducing a proportionality constant, λ, and indicating a decrease in activity with a negative sign, this equation becomes

$$\frac{dN}{dt} = - \lambda N \tag{2}$$

Perhaps an analogy will help us to understand the nature of the "first order" process described by this equation. If we visualize a reservoir of water with an outlet at the bottom, it can be shown that the rate of flow from the outlet is proportional to the height of the column of water in the reservoir (Fig. 5.1). The height of the water corresponds to the number of radioactive atoms in the sample with the size of the outlet pipe determining the proportionality constant which corresponds to the decay constant in the radioactivity case.

In radioactivity calculations, the expression dN/dt is the

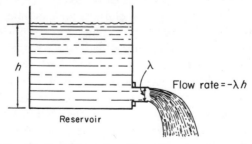

Fig. 5.1. Reservoir analogy for radioactive decay of radioactive sample decaying to stable daughter.

disintegration rate of the sample. The term "activity" is sometimes used to refer to this true disintegration rate although activity is used somewhat ambiguously, and often refers to a measured quantity, e.g., counts per minute, which is proportional to the disintegration rate.

It can be seen that it is possible to calculate the weight of radioactive material which gives a certain disintegration rate from Eq. (2). The results of a few of these calculations are given in Table 5.1.

TABLE 5.1.   Quantities of Radioactive Material Giving 10^8 Disintegrations per Second

Isotope	Half Life	Quantity (grams)
U^{238}	4.5×10^9 years	8100
C^{14}	5680 years	8×10^{-5}
Ru^{106}	1 year	8.4×10^{-7}
As^{76}	26.5 hours	1.5×10^{-9}
In^{116}	54 minutes	9.3×10^{-11}
F^{17}	66 seconds	3.4×10^{-13}

It should be noted that a counting sample used in making a measurement of these materials may be as low as 10 dps or less. The actual weights of material in a counting sample are thus 10^{-7} times the weights indicated above. This means that in a typical counting sample of In^{116}, for example, there are only of the order of 10^{-18} gm. This is many powers of ten lower than the limits of chemical detection. From a chemical point of view, "carrier free" samples of these short-lived materials are weightless. Even when a sample is carrier free, it might contain more stable atoms arising from the dust of the room, etc., than from the active sample. It must be remembered, however, that when samples are produced by the (n, γ) reaction there is always a very large number of atoms present which did not capture neutrons and which remain as nuclei of stable isotopes in the sample.

It is of interest to calculate the weights of such radioactive samples, but this is not the usual problem to be considered in the nuclear laboratory. The investigator usually wishes to know instead, the activity of the sample at some time other than that of his initial measurement. To solve this problem, it is usually desirable to express the rate equation in an integrated form rather than in the differential form given in Eq. (2). Integration of Eq. (2) gives the following result:

$$\mathcal{N} = \mathcal{N}_0 e^{-\lambda t} \tag{3}$$

in which $\mathcal{N}_0$ is the number of radioactive atoms at some reference time, $\mathcal{N}$ is the number of radioactive atoms at any other time, t, with λ being the disintegration constant, and e the base of natural logarithms. A graph of this curve gives the well-known exponential curve which can be plotted either as disintegrations per second on a linear or on a semilogarithmic plot as in Fig. 5.2. These equations also apply to quantities proportional to the number of radioactive atoms present such

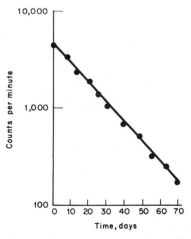

Fig. 5.2. Plot of radioactive decay of single radionuclide ($T\frac{1}{2}$ = 14 days).

as the disintegration rate or counting rate of a sample. This relationship could then be expressed $A = A_0\, e^{-\lambda t}$ in which A and A_0 are the activities of the sample at the two times.

Eq. (3) shows that the proportion of the atoms disintegrating is constant for any given period of time. This means that a certain fraction of the atoms, one-third, for example, would decay in a given period of time. For convenience, the time required for one half of the atoms to decay is frequently designated. This is called the half life for which we frequently use the symbol $T_{\frac{1}{2}}$. The half life, the time required for the ratio N/N_0 to become equal to $\frac{1}{2}$, may be expressed in terms of the disintegration constant as follows:

$$N = N_0\, e^{-\lambda t} \tag{4}$$

$$\frac{N}{N_0} = \frac{1}{2} = e^{-\lambda T_{\frac{1}{2}}} \tag{5}$$

By taking natural logarithms of both sides of the equation, we have

$$\ln\frac{1}{2} = -\lambda T_{\frac{1}{2}}$$

or
$$\ln 2 = \lambda T_{\frac{1}{2}}$$

By inserting the value for the natural logarithm of 2, we have

$$T_{\frac{1}{2}} = \frac{0.693}{\lambda} \tag{6}$$

$$\lambda = \frac{0.693}{T_{\frac{1}{2}}} \tag{7}$$

The value of the half life can be determined either from the equations by the introduction of the measured activity at two different times or by graphical methods from the decay measurements when they are plotted on a semilogarithmic curve. Likewise, we can ascertain the change in the activity for any time interval either by inserting the time interval into the equation or by using the graph of activity vs. time. We might mention that the same mathematical relationship holds for the half thickness in relation to the absorption coefficient (see Chapter 3), since the change in intensity of γ radiation varies exponentially with a variation in filter thickness.

There are some types of calculations in which it is useful to know the average life of all the individual atoms in a radioactive sample. This is found to be equal to 1.44 times the half life.

The above equations are those which describe the decay of a pure radioactive species. If one has a mixture of two or more radioactive elements, each will exhibit its own decay independently of the other and the curve describing the decay would then show an inflection or change in slope. An example of such a mixture of two isotopes is shown in Fig. 5.3. The half lives of the two components can be determined graphically by the extrapolation of the longer-lived component back to zero time and subtracting this extrapolated curve from the total curve. One can obtain the half life of the longer-lived component by inspection of the extrapolated curve, and the shorter-lived component by inspection of the subtracted curve (drawn through the triangular points in Fig. 5.3).

Decay of a Radioactive Parent and Radioactive Daughter

In the cases described above, the radioactive atoms were assumed to have decayed to a stable nuclide of another element. If, on the other hand, the daughter nucleus is also radioactive, it is possible to determine the amount of radioactivity resulting from the decay of the daughter atoms. This is an important calculation in the study both of the naturally

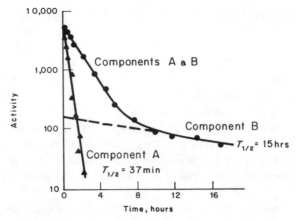

Fig. 5.3. Plot of radioactive decay of two independently decaying radionuclides.

occurring decay chains and of the series of radioactive products of nuclear fission. For example, Sr^{90} with a half life of 25 years gives rise to Y^{90} which has a half life of 65 hours. Both of these radioelements contribute to the biological damage observed when fission products are ingested into the body.

The reservoir analogy described earlier also shows the nature of this type of calculation. In this case, we now visualize several reservoirs each with an outlet emptying into the next. The sizes of the various outlets correspond to the decay constants, λ_1, λ_2, etc., of the various members of the radioactive chain. The amount of water in any of the reservoirs could then be determined by calculations involving the amount of water originally present and the rates of flow from each of the reservoirs. This is illustrated in Fig. 5.4.

If we let P_0 represent the number of radioactive parent atoms with disintegration constant, λ_1, at some initial time, P would then represent the number of atoms of this kind of material at any other time, t. Similarly, let us represent by Q, the number of atoms of the radioactive daughter element

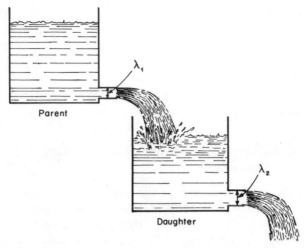

Fig. 5.4. Reservoir analogy for decay of a radioactive chain.

with disintegration constant, λ_2, at the end of the same time period. Then

$$Q = \frac{P_0\lambda_1(e^{-\lambda_1 t} - e^{-\lambda_2 t})}{\lambda_2 - \lambda_1} \tag{8}$$

The activity of the daughter is found by multiplying the number of radioactive atoms in the sample by its disintegration constant, λ_2.

One important result of this type of calculation is that when the half life of the parent is very long relative to the half life of the daughter and when the daughter remains with the parent sample, a condition of "secular equilibrium" is reached. At this point, the decay rate of the daughter becomes equal to that of the parent and thus the activity of the two radioactive materials becomes equal. Advantage of this relationship is taken in the case of Ra^{226} with a half life of 1620 years, and its Rn^{222} daughter which has a half life of 3.8 days. If one has a millicurie (roughly one milligram) of Ra^{226}, the daughter activity continues to increase for 40 days, although the growth is much more rapid at first and may be almost insignificant later. The sample then contains one millicurie (but not one milligram) of the daughter radon. The radon, being a gas, may be pumped off and distributed in the form of radon tubes for medical use, while the radium builds up an equivalent amount of radon again.

PART B. THE STATISTICAL ASPECTS OF RADIOACTIVITY MEASUREMENT

In the previous section of this chapter, we considered the mathematical aspects of the radioactive decay processes. It was emphasized that these laws that give rise to such concepts as half life, average life, etc., are entirely statistical in nature and are valid only when large numbers of radioactive atoms are under consideration. It is interesting to note that, whereas the common extension of the half-life concept is that the radioactive material *never* decays because of the exponential character of the decay curve, in reality all of the material actually does eventually decay. The last few atoms do not follow the decay-law generalization, but we know that each unstable atom will eventually disintegrate.

The statistical nature of these laws becomes clearly evident upon the measurement of a radioactive sample. A number of repetitive counts on a sample shows that there is a deviation in the observed counting rates even when the counting conditions are kept constant. This gives rise to one of the most important aspects of work with radioactive materials—the variability and reliability of the experimental results obtained from the measurement of a random-decay process.

An important part of the reporting of the results of any experiment should be an indication of the reliability of the results. This is particularly so when slightly different results would lead to major differences in the interpretation of the experiment. There are several general sources of errors in any type of laboratory work. A list of these would include errors in the measurement of volumes and weights, losses resulting from chemical separations, losses resulting from transfer operations, the presence of impurities, and variations in other laboratory conditions, manipulations, and arithmetical calculations.

The very nature of the process of radioactive decay and the properties of the radiations emitted lead to errors in radioactivity measurements not found, for example, in the usual chemical measurements. Following are some of these sources of uncertainty: (1) the random nature of the disintegration process; (2) errors arising in the detection operations—coincidence losses, variation in performance of detectors such as the observation of spurious counts, or of electronic, mechanical, or timing components of the measurement system; and (3) the variations in radiation measurement technique, including variations in absorption and the scattering of the radiation by materials on the sample or its surroundings. The relative importance of the various factors listed above varies with the type of measurement being conducted, and the type of apparatus used.

Errors such as the ones listed above could be classified either as systematic or as accidental errors. The former are minimized by applying known calibration factors—for example, allowance for a chemical yield less than 100% can be made on the basis of results obtained for a standard sample. Similarly, the efficiency of a radiation detector may be determined by calibration of the detector with a standard radiation source.

Even when allowance is made for all systematic or determinate errors, the values obtained from a set of supposedly identical experiments will show some variation. For example, samples measured with a very carefully calibrated pipet will show small variations in volume even when extreme care is exercised. These accidental errors may be minimized by careful experimental technique.

It will be recalled that an error, e, in a measured value, X, is defined as follows:

$$e = X - T$$

where T is the true or correct value. The magnitude of e is a measurement of the *accuracy* of the measured value. Actually, the true value is never known with absolute certainty, so that an error, so defined can never be calculated. Instead, the difference between each measured value of a set of measurements and the best approximation to the true value is calculated. If only accidental errors are assumed, the best approximation to the true value is the arithmetic mean value, $\overline{X}$, of the set of measurements. The difference, x, is then referred to as a deviation which is defined by the expression

$$x = X - \overline{X}$$

The value of the arithmetic mean is obtained by the usual summation and division process. The magnitude of the deviation, x, for a particular measured value is an indication of the *precision* or reproducibility of the result. General usage is such that a measure of precision is also taken as a satisfactory measure of accuracy. It is true, of course, that good accuracy demands good precision but, on the other hand, good precision does not guarantee high accuracy. For example, a set of measured values may show very little scatter about the average, but the average value itself may differ greatly from the true value because of a systematic error.

If the frequency of occurrence of values obtained in a very large number of identical measurements subject to random accidental errors are plotted along the ordinate and the corresponding values along the abscissa, a frequency distribution curve is obtained. Such a curve is generally bellshaped, with the mean value as the most probable one having a frequency of occurrence at the peak of the curve. Such a typical frequency curve for deviations is shown in Fig. 5.5.

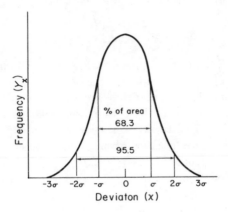

Fig. 5.5. Frequency distribution curve showing deviations from an average value.

Several distribution laws have been formulated to represent frequency distribution curves. Each of these distribution equations has its own specific application, but because it is relatively easy to handle mathematically, the normal distribution law is frequently used as an approximation for the others.

According to the normal distribution law, positive and negative deviations of a given magnitude are equally probable, and the occurrence of large deviations is less probable than that of small ones. This corresponds to the symmetrical bell-shaped curve with the most probable value as the arithmetic average. From the distribution curve for the deviations of a set of measured values about the average, the probability may be calculated for the occurrence of a deviation as large as or larger than some specified value.   Several measures of precision or "error" are used to indicate the reliability of a result. These are usually based on the usage of the "standard deviation."   This may be defined as follows: *For any measured value X in a set of n measured values having a mean,* $\overline{X}$,

$$SD = \sigma_x = \left(\sum \frac{(x - x)^2}{n - 1} \right)^{\frac{1}{2}}$$

A plot of this quantity is shown in Fig. 5.5.   The figure shows that 68.3% of the area under the curve lies within the limits of $+\sigma$ and $-\sigma$.   This means that measured values will be expected to fall between these two limits 68.3% of the time. The other 31.7% of the time they would be expected to fall at limits that are greater or less than these.   It will be noted that the probable error (50% error) is about 67% of the standard deviation.   This means that the measured values would be expected to fall within this narrower range on 50% of the trials.   Other commonly used measures of precision in radioactive measurements are the nine-tenths error (NTE) and the 0.95 error.   These limits are respectively 1.65 σ_x and 1.95 σ_x.   It should be clear that the larger the error specified the greater the chance that a measured value will lie within the specified limits.   It is important to indicate which of the many precision measures is being reported with an experimental result.   For simplicity in the following discussion, we will use the standard deviation as the measure of precision. Other corresponding measures can be determined by the use of appropriate constants.

Statistics of Counting Radioactivity

When a person makes a measurement to obtain the total number of counts, N, on a sample, he usually does not make a large number of repeated counts. Rather, he makes only one count for a long enough time to obtain a statistically significant number of counts. The result that he obtains is merely an approximation of the true average count that he would obtain, if he had counted for many time intervals, of the size that he used in making his count. From his count he can set up limits within which he can specify a given statistical chance of including the true average count for the sample in question. It can be shown that the standard deviation for a large number of events or counts is given by the square root of the total number of counts measured; that is, if one measures 100 events (counts), the standard deviation is ± 10 (10%), while if a total of 10,000 counts are measured, the standard deviation is ± 100 (1%).

Let us take an example. Assume that the true average counting rate of a sample is 100 counts per minute, and that a one-minute count on the sample yields 90 counts, which is one standard deviation below the true average. The 90 counts is the best estimate that the researcher has for the true average count that he would obtain in one minute on the sample. However, he knows that this is not the true average count. He can then set up limits in which he will have a 68.3% chance of including the true average count. This is the square root of the number of counts that he observed. He would then state that the counting rate on the sample is 90 ± 9.5 counts per minute with a 68.3% chance of including the true average counting rate. He would thus come within 0.5 count per minute of including the true average. If he sets his limits to two times the standard deviation, he would say that the true average counting rate fell in the interval 90 ± 19 counts per minute with a 95% chance of being correct.

In order to have more confidence in his results, he should count for a longer period of time so that he would make more observations (counts) on his sample. If he counted for 10 minutes he might obtain, for example, 1030 counts. He could then say with 68.3% confidence that the true average count for 10 minutes on the sample was 1030 ± 32 counts. To give his results in counts per minute, he would then divide both the counts and the one sigma limit by 10 and obtain 103 ± 3.2 counts per minute. The limits for 95% confidence would, of course, be twice this deviation or ± 6.4 counts per minute. The procedure for 68.3% confidence may be generalized as follows:

Standard deviation of count: $\sqrt{N}$

Standard deviation of counting rate:

$$\frac{\sqrt{N}}{t} = \frac{\sqrt{Rt}}{t} = \sqrt{\frac{R}{t}}$$

where N = total counts observed, and t = length of counting period in minutes; $R = N/t$ = counts per minute.

The standard deviation of the difference, $N_1 - N_2$, e.g., the total counting rate of a sample minus the background rate, between two counts made during time intervals of the same length, is the square root of the *sum* of the squares of the standard deviations of the individual counts.

chapter six

APPLICATIONS OF NUCLEAR CHEMISTRY

Introduction

We have considered the major principles and concepts of nuclear chemistry in the preceding chapters. The applications of this fascinating field range far and wide, and we have chosen only a few of these areas to illustrate the diversity involved in utilizing the results and techniques developed in nuclear chemistry.

Fission and Fusion Weapons

It is, perhaps, unfortunate that the advent of nuclear science first burst on the world in an explosion over Hiroshima. Since that time, the first reaction of most people to atomic or nuclear problems is one of fear, partly caused by the intangibility of radiation and the uncertainty as to the amount and nature of some of the potential biological radiation effects, along with an assumed complexity of the nuclear field.

From a scientific point of view, the use of fission or fusion in a weapon is not complicated, and is based on the principles of binding energy, which were discussed in Chapter 1. It was pointed out in that chapter that energy is given off when elements of high atomic number are broken down into their nucleons, and that energy is given off if larger nuclei are formed by combining light ones. The problems are the technological ones as to how to bring about these processes in a practical device.

The construction of an atomic or fission bomb involves obtaining, at a desired time, a critical amount of a somewhat rare isotope of uranium, U^{235}, or of plutonium, Pu^{239} (U^{233} is also fissionable, but it must be prepared synthetically, usually from Th^{232}). The U^{235} isotope occurs in nature with about 0.7% abundance, with essentially all of the remaining uranium being U^{238}. It was pointed out in Chapter 3 that U^{235} will undergo fission when it captures a slow neutron, giving rise to two fragments and two or three neutrons. If these neutrons can be utilized to fission further uranium nuclei, it is possible to obtain a chain reaction in which more neutrons are given off than are used up in a given generation. The critical amount of U^{235} is the amount of the isotope that is required to bring about a self-sustaining nuclear chain reaction, and is less than a kilogram of pure U^{235}. An atomic bomb contains the required quantity of U^{235}, together with the components necessary to keep the uranium mass at a subcritical level (usually by keeping the various portions of uranium at a distance from one another) and the parts of the device needed to bring the critical amounts of uranium close together when desired. About 200 Mev of energy is liberated for each fission, most of which is given as kinetic energy to the fission fragments. While the amount of energy from one nuclear fission is not high by ordinary standards, if the weapon is designed to fission, say 10^{20} nuclei, the resulting energy release is beyond comprehension.

It is of considerable significance that fission can be brought about by the capture of a slow neutron. On the other hand, the liberation of energy in the fusion process requires the use of very high temperatures to overcome the high fusion potential barrier. A fusion or hydrogen bomb could utilize the fusion of deuterium or tritium nuclei. Once the barrier is penetrated by the nuclei a great deal more energy is available than that required to start the reaction, so the amount of energy given off is much greater than is required to initiate the reaction. If the igniting temperature is reached, a self-sustaining chain reaction will likewise continue so long as material is available for fusion, and so long as the temperature is at or above the ignition point. Fortunately for weapon technology, the atomic or fission bomb is a readily available device for producing the ignition temperature, and the fission (atomic) bomb is used as a "fuse" for starting the reaction chain. Although in principle there would be no limit to the size of such a weapon, in practice the high temperatures serve to separate the hydrogen molecules, and it is not easy to keep these materials confined to the region where fusion can take place. Since fission products are usually radioactive, it is evident that some "fallout" of these fragments will be produced by the detonation of both types of weapons. Fusion products are not ordinarily radioactive, so the fallout from a hydrogen fusion device contains only the fallout from the fission bomb "trigger" along with materials which are made radioactive by capture of the neutrons from the various reactions.

Atoms for Peace

The basic scientific principles utilized in the production of weapons have also been applied quite widely for constructive purposes. The statement has been made that already more lives have been saved by the peacetime applications of nuclear science that have been lost in wartime uses of nuclear weapons. The use of fission to generate useful heat and power has already been accomplished through use of nuclear reactors. In these devices a critical amount of fissionable material is stacked together with some "moderator" material (e.g., heavy water or graphite) which can slow down the fission neutrons to permit easier capture by the other fissionable atoms. The rate of the chain reaction is controlled by the insertion of cadmium or boron steel rods, since both cadmium and boron capture neutrons readily. The energy of the controlled chain reaction appears primarily as heat, and can be removed from the reactor by circulating some type of coolant to provide heat for steam turbines. Since gamma radiation and neutrons are also produced in copious quantities, thick radiation shielding of concrete or water usually surrounds the reactor "core." It has been estimated that the fission of 1 lb of U^{235} liberates the heat equivalent of more than 1000 tons of coal. While the major technological problems of producing atomic power have been solved, such power is only beginning to be economically competitive in the U. S. Some efforts are being made now for the direct conversion of fission energy to electricity without using the steam generation step.

A great deal of effort is being given to the attempt to develop a controlled nuclear fusion or thermonuclear device, as it is usually called. Some of the reactions that could be used in this process include the following:

$$d^2 + d^2 \longrightarrow He^3 + n^1 \tag{1}$$

$$d^2 + d^2 \longrightarrow H^3 + p^1 \tag{2}$$

$$d^2 + t^3 \longrightarrow He^4 + n^1 \tag{3}$$

By making binding energy calculations as was done in Chapter 2, it can be shown that reaction (1) above would give off 3.2 Mev energy reaction, (2) would release 4.0 Mev energy while reaction (3) would produce 17.6 Mev energy. Although hydrogen is one of the most plentiful elements on the earth, only one atom in 6000 is deuterium. Tritium must be prepared by a suitable nuclear reaction before it can enter into the fusion reaction as described. The thermonuclear energy theoretically available in fusion reactions is fantastically high, since the energy that could be released from the small amount of deuterium in a gallon of ordinary water would be equivalent to the heat produced by burning 300 gallons of gasoline. Likewise, the fusion reactions have the advantage over fission processes in that no radioactive fission products are produced.

The essential problems to be solved in obtaining useful energy from fusion are fourfold: (1) A suitable fuel must be available. This involves the separation and enrichment of deuterium from ordinary water or the production of tritium in a nuclear reactor. (2) The particles must be heated to temperatures of from 50 to 100 million degrees depending on the particular reaction employed. Although this seems very high as a thermal temperature, it can be shown that 100 million degrees correspond to a particle energy of about 10,000 electron volts. In a nuclear frame of reference, it is not difficult to accelerate a particle to an energy of 10 Kev. Materials at these temperatures no longer have electrons attached to their atoms, and the high temperature system is referred to as a plasma. It is important that the entire plasma have the required fusion energy in order for a continuing reaction to take place.

Problem (3) is to contain the plasma for a long enough time to allow a substantial portion of the nuclei present in the plasma to undergo fusion. The containment problem will doubtless be solved using strong magnetic fields as magnetic "bottles" to allow the fusion to take place. Problem (4) is the practical one of how to harness the released energy in order to generate useful power.

Transuranium Elements

The fantastically small scale of experiments in this area of nuclear chemistry represents one of the most imaginative aspects of modern chemistry. Mention was made in Chapter 2 of the processes by which elements with atomic number higher than that of uranium could be observed following the beta decay of certain uranium isotopes. Since these processes involve changes in individual atoms, one transmutation experiment involved separating one atom of mendelevium (at. no. 101) from about one billion atoms of einsteinium (at. no. 99). The billion atoms in the sample represented less than 10^{-13} gm of the element.

Although in a sense atomic fission itself was a dividend or by-product of man's quest for the transuranium elements, the most immediate effect of these discoveries of new elements was the use of plutonium in nuclear weapons. However, the basic research done has had other important applications, including the use of certain isotopes of transuranium elements as concentrated sources of power. The first use of nuclear power in space was the incorporation of a source of plutonium-238 in a TRANSIT satellite (1961) in which the heat from the radioactive source produced electricity in a thermocouple system.

As an example of the type of nuclear chemical work which has been performed in this field, we might describe the experiments in which several of these elements were produced and identified. One of these involved an experiment to measure the energies of the two main fission fragments from the neutron-induced fission of U^{235}. A thin layer of uranium oxide was placed on one piece of paper and next to this were stacked layers of cigarette paper to determine the range of the fragments as they recoiled. One of the experimenters observed that there was one product which did not recoil enough to leave the original paper support. After suspecting that this was a product formed by the capture of a neutron in the uranium, these workers were able to show by chemical processes that this product was an isotope of neptunium (at. no. 93). The chemical investigations showed that the element resembled uranium and not rhenium as would be expected from the older periodic table. This conclusion gave rise to a new series of "rare earth" type elements, the actinide series, which are analogous to the previously known rare earth group, the lanthanide series.

In another famous group of experiments, it was postulated that element 102 could be produced by the bombardment of element 96 (curium). The calculations indicated that if all of the available supply of curium were used in one experiment, it might be possible to produce one atom of element 102. The experiment was performed 21 times with an atom of the new element being detected in 17 of the experiments. The identification of this element was carried out using these 17 radioactive atoms.

The reactions which first produced the transuranium elements are shown in Table 6.1.

TABLE 6.1. Reactions Producing the Transuranium Elements

Atomic number	Name	Symbol	Production reaction
93	Neptunium	Np	$U^{238} + n \rightarrow Np^{239} + \beta^-$
94	Plutonium	Pu	$U^{238} + d \rightarrow Pu^{240} + \beta^-$
95	Americium	Am	$Pu^{239} + n \rightarrow Am^{240} + \beta^-$
96	Curium	Cm	$Pu^{239} + He^4 \rightarrow Cm^{242} + \eta$
97	Berkelium	Bk	$Am^{241} + He^4 \rightarrow Bk^{243} + 2n$
98	Californium	Cf	$Cm^{242} + He^4 \rightarrow Cf^{245} + n$
99	Einsteinium	E	$U^{238} + 15n \rightarrow E^{253} + 7\beta^-$ (H bomb)
100	Fermium	Fm	$U^{238} + 17n \rightarrow Fm^{255} + 8\beta$ (H bomb)
101	Mendelevium	Mv	$E^{253} + He^4 \rightarrow Mv^{256} + n$
102	(Nobelium)*	(No)	$Cm^{246} + C^{12} \rightarrow No^{254} + 6n$
103	Lawrencium	Lw	$Cf^{246} + B^{11} \rightarrow Lw^{257}$

*Name not officially accepted.

It is possible that a half dozen or so new transuranium elements may be synthesized, separated and identified; but barring unknown experimental breakthroughs or unknown regions of stability in these heavier elements, it is expected that the end of the search for new elements should come somewhere in the region of element 110. The elements up to and including einsteinium have isotopes sufficiently long-lived to be isolated in macroscopic, that is, weighable quantities, but this does not seem to be true beyond einsteinium. Unfortunately for the prospect of producing ever-higher elements, the longest-lived isotopes that can be made beyond elements 104 and 105 will probably not exist long enough for conventional chemical identification.

However, it appears that the prediction of the chemical properties of the yet undiscovered chemical elements is quite straightforward. Lawrencium completes the actinide series, and it is expected that elements 104, 105, 106, etc. will be fitted into the periodic table under hafnium, tantalum, tungsten, etc., and will have analogous chemical properties.

Radioisotopes—Practical Nuclear Chemistry

One of the "by-products" of a nuclear reactor is the production of radioisotopes either in the fission process itself, or in the introduction of other materials into the neutron atmosphere of the reactor. Many hundreds of radioisotopes are known, and a hundred or more have sufficiently long half lives that they can be produced in a reactor and shipped to research laboratories for further use. It is in this area that nuclear science has contributed most significantly to the welfare of mankind, and it is a rare field of scientific research that does not have the possibility of using radioactive isotopes as a tool. In general, if the problem to be studied involves a determination of the quantity of material present, its rate of movement and its subsequent location, radioisotopes can potentially offer assistance. This, of course, is not true for determinations of oxygen and nitrogen which have singular importance in biological and biochemical fields, but the use of stable isotope tracers of these elements make them of interest also to nuclear chemists. New instruments using fast neutron reactions can extend the usefulness of many of the nuclear techniques to a still wider area of applications. Many workers are concerned with radioactivity as applied to a problem in their own area of specialization such as medicine, agriculture, or industry. There are numerous special applications of radioactivity to analytical chemistry and, in particular, there are two chemical techniques which rely specifically on the nuclear properties of the materials. These are isotope dilution and activation analysis.

Radioactivity and Analytical Chemistry

A primary reason for the great utility of radioisotopes is their high sensitivity to detection. This detectability is fundamentally related to the fact that in samples having intermediate half lives ranging from hours to years, the amount of radioactive element present in a counting sample is of the order of 10^{-16} to 10^{-19} gm. It is evident, however, that in no case can one actually have such a "carrier-free" sample, for all materials are trace contaminated by other elements. Nonetheless, under certain conditions it is possible to detect 10^{-11} to 10^{-14} gm of a number of common elements. Radioactivity provides a tool of sensitivity, and is of importance because of its application in analytical processes.

Among the various uses for radioactivity in the techniques of analytical chemistry are activity analysis and radiometric analysis. The term "activity analysis" refers to the simple determination of the amount of radioactive material in a sample; "radiometric analysis," to the assay of a given non-radioactive substance by the addition of a radioactive tracer. For example, silver could be determined directly in a sample by analysis of radioactive silver, or the amount of silver could be ascertained by radiometric analysis in which AgCl was precipitated with radioactive chloride ions.

The term "radiochemistry" is often used for this type of work, but is not entirely standardized. Many workers apply the term to the use of radioactivity in the study of any type of chemical process. Others prefer to employ it only when discussing the direct investigations of radioactive materials— for example, studies of fission-product chemistry, of transuranium elements, and of the inorganic chemistry of elements such as technetium and promethium which are available only in the radioactive form. It is probably not necessary to make a precise description, since little ambiguity arises in the various fields.

Radioactive material employed as an analytical tool is the foundation of the bulk of work with radioisotopes. The ability to trace radioactive materials through one of a wide range of chemical and physical systems is essentially based on the high analytical sensitivity inherent in the localization and measurement of exceedingly small amounts of material. The application of radioactive and stable isotope tracers is the subject of many books and papers in practically every field of scientific research. Thus, a compilation of scientific papers published in 1958 by the U. S. A.E.C. listed over 7000 published in five years on radioisotopes. A smaller but important number of papers recorded investigations involving stable isotopes in which the assay of the samples was commonly performed with a mass spectrometer.

Isotope Dilution

Of course, radioactive or stable tracers are invaluable for the quick and easy solution of general analytical problems. However, it is also worth noting that two special analytical tools are related to the nuclear properties of certain materials. The first of these special techniques, applicable to both radioactive and stable nuclides, is called isotope dilution analysis. The principle of this method, which is quite simple, is based on the assumption that tracers follow the same chemical or physical path followed by the nontracer atoms. For example, the determination of the blood volume of a patient may be an important medical diagnostic aid. Suppose a saline solution containing a certain amount of an isotope, e.g., Cr^{51}-labeled blood cells, were given to a patient, and the blood allowed to circulate until the radioactive cells were uniformly mixed with the nonlabeled cells. Then, assume that a sample of a certain volume of blood was taken, and its radioactivity measured. It is easy to see that the volume of blood then containing the original amount of tracer can be calculated directly from the proportion of the radioactive sample measured.

The problem is somewhat more complex, however, if the material added has a measurable amount of the stable isotope of the tracer. In this case, it is necessary to know the specific activity (e.g., cpm/mg) of the added tracer material, and the specific activity of the final material must be determined. This technique is particularly useful in cases in which it is relatively easy to make a partial separation of the compound of interest, but very difficult to make accurate quantitative separations.

Activation Analysis

The second analytical technique employing specifically nuclear properties is activation analysis. We mentioned earlier that if a sample of any material is placed in a neutron atmosphere in a reactor or a neutron generator, some of the nuclei will capture neutrons. If the (n, γ) reaction produces radioactive nuclei, these will then decay with the appropriate half life of the radioisotope. The decay rate in disintegrations per second when the material is taken from the reactor is given by the following equation:

$$A = f N \sigma S$$

in which the activity, A, is given in disintegrations per second, and f is the "flux" or the number of neutrons per cm² per second at the sample position. N is the number of target atoms in the sample, σ is the "cross section" in cm² and S is a saturation factor including the half life of the radioactive isotope and the time of bombardment. The number of target atoms, N, is given by

$$N = \frac{\text{weight in grams of target atoms}}{\text{gram atomic weight}} \times 6.02 \times 10^{23}$$

The cross section, σ, is frequently of the order of 10^{-24} cm². This has given rise to the use of the term "barn" which is a common unit of cross section, and is defined as 1×10^{-24} cm². S is given by the expression $(1 - \exp\{-0.693t/T_{\frac{1}{2}}\})$ in which $T_{\frac{1}{2}}$ is the half life of the radioactive isotope formed, and t is the time of bombardment.

The activity of the sample at any time after being removed from the neutron source may be determined by making the usual calculations or graphical solutions for compensating for radioactive decay (Chapter 5).

Let us consider the irradiation of 1 gm of gold (Au^{197}) for 3.8 days (one half life of Au^{198}) as an example. Assume that the reactor flux is 1×10^{-12} n/cm²/sec. The cross section for this reaction is 96 barns.

$$\text{Activity} = \underset{\text{dps}}{\left(\underset{\text{n/cm}^2/\text{sec}}{1 \times 10^{12}}\right)} \left(\underset{\text{atoms/gm of Au}}{\frac{1}{197} \times 6.02 \times 10^{23}}\right)$$
$$\times \underset{\text{cm}^2}{(96 \times 10^{-24})} \underset{\text{days}}{(1 - \exp\{-0.693 \times 3.8/3.8\})}$$

This gives an activity of about 1.5×10^{11} dps or 4 curies of activity produced. According to the calculations shown in Chapter 5, this amount represents 2/100 of one milligram (2×10^{-5} gm) of radioactive Au^{198} which would be dispersed in the gram of stable Au^{197}. This represents a very small fraction of the target mass which has been made radioactive. On the other hand, since we are able to measure activities of the order of 1 dps, this means that we could dilute the gram of material ten billion times, and still be able to detect its presence.

The activation analysis method uses the reverse of the above calculation. Suppose we wished to analyze a sample of some material in which gold was an impurity. The sample would then be irradiated in the neutron source. If there were some way, then, of measuring the radioactive gold independently of other radioactivity in the sample, we would have a direct measure of the amount of gold present. Sometimes the only activity observed would be that produced by the element of interest if the other materials in the sample have such short half lives that they decay away first. At other times it is necessary to make chemical separations of the impurity from the remainder of the sample. (It should also be noted that it is possible to add nonradioactive gold to the sample after the irradiation in order to have large enough quantities to manipulate chemically. This added material would not contribute to the measured radioactivity.) A very powerful method for measuring only one component in a mixture of radioactive materials is by the electronic sorting of the various radiations using a pulse height analyzer (Chapter 4). It can be seen that activation analysis, in principle, can be used to determine hundredths of parts per billion of gold in a sample. Many other analyses are also highly sensitive, but one great advantage of this method is that it can be applied to a sample in any chemical or physical state, since these factors do not affect the radioactivity produced.

Specialized Radiochemical Problems

Among the specialized problems of interest to nuclear chemists is age dating. This might involve dating very old material such as ores, ocean cores, and sediments. However, age dating might also concern itself with more recent periods, as would be the case in the dating of carbon 14-containing materials and meteorite dating. In general, all of these studies involve the very low-level measurement of radioactivity. Backgrounds of a few counts per hour have been obtained using rather sophisticated electronic techniques. Such low backgrounds would be required, for example, to measure the natural carbon-14 in a sample of present-day organic material which has a specific activity of about 15.3 disintegrations per minute per gram, and even more care would be required to date old samples with less radioactivity in them.

The Isotope Effect

It has been pointed out that the major use of radioactive isotopes has been in research, utilizing these materials as tracers. One of the basic assumptions in tracer work is the assumption that the chemical behavior of the radioactive species is identical to that of the corresponding stable isotope. The so-called isotope effect must be considered, however, in certain types of experiments. The assumption mentioned is only approximately correct, since the masses of the nuclei vary and, according to kinetic theory, the rates of movement of atoms of different masses differ. If the energy of the two atoms is the same, it can be shown that their velocities would vary inversely as the square root of their masses. It is apparent that this difference in rate would be quite considerable with H^1 and H^3 with a rate difference of 73% being expected. The rate difference between C^{14} and C^{12} would be about 7%, but this factor would represent a difference of only about 1.5% between I^{131} and I^{127}. The mass differences exert their effect primarily on the rates of reactions, and would be less important if equilibrium has been reached.

Recent studies indicate that another possible difference in reactivity may be observed for different isotopes of the same element. It appears that there is an actual difference in bond strengths between bonds formed with different isotopes. If this is the case, there might well be a considerable difference in specificity for reactions involving the formation or breaking of certain bonds. This problem has not been well worked out, but it should be considered in more detail in chemical reaction mechanism studies when radioisotopes are used.

Radiation Chemistry

Although not related directly to the primary problems of nuclear chemistry, the effects of radiation on chemical systems is one of considerable importance, particularly in biological and biochemical studies. It may well be that the use of radiation as an initiator of desirable reactions may be extended to reactions such as the industrial chlorination of benzene in which radiation functions something like a catalyst.

Much of the theory of radiation chemistry has been developed from the general problems of radiation effects on living systems. This is not a problem at the low levels of radiation usually employed in laboratory procedures, but it is exceedingly important to the over-all nuclear and radiation fields.

There have been two general approaches to the concept of biological radiation damage. One of these is referred to as the "target" theory. This concept is that radiation damage is caused by direct hits of the radiation on the biologically significant component such as the chromosome or gene. The other concept is that the radiation damage is caused by chemical effects produced by changes in the chemical environment of the cell. Since water makes up a large portion of the biological system, the radiation chemistry of water is considered exceedingly important, and has been studied extensively. The present consensus is that the chemical effects are the most important factors in biological radiation damage.

As in any complex chemical system, a number of competing reactions may be observed when radiation interacts with water. When heavy radiation particles such as alpha particles, deuterons, and protons interact with water, two of the possible reactions are the following:

$$2 \, H_2O \rightarrow H_2 + H_2O_2$$
$$2 \, H_2O \rightarrow 2 \, H + H_2O_2$$

The predominating initial reaction for particles such as beta particles and secondary electrons from gamma or X-ray interactions is probably the following:

$$2 \, H_2O \rightarrow H_2 + 2 \, OH$$

One of the important aspects in these reactions is seen to be the production of "free radicals" which subsequently react with other radicals or molecules of the system. Free radicals may be described as fragments of molecules containing an odd number of electrons. They have a fleeting existence, but it is assumed that most chemical and biological effects are brought about by the reaction of aqueous free radicals with the other components of the cell. Some of the free radicals formed in this way are H, OH, and HO_2. Considerable effort is being expended in elucidating the ways in which these radicals are formed and the ways in which they interact with cell components.

SELECTED REFERENCES

LABORATORY TECHNIQUES

Chase, G. D., "Principles of Radioisotope Methodology," Burgess Publishing Co., Minneapolis, 1959.

Choppin, G. R., "Experimental Nuclear Chemistry," Prentice-Hall, Inc., Englewood Cliffs, N. J., 1961.

Overman, R. T., and Clark, H. M., "Radioisotope Techniques," McGraw-Hill Book Co., Inc., New York, 1960.

THEORETICAL MATERIAL

Evans, R. D., "The Atomic Nucleus," McGraw-Hill Book Co., Inc., New York, 1955.

Friedlander, G., and Kennedy, J. W., "Nuclear and Radiochemistry," John Wiley & Sons, Inc., New York, 1955.

Gamow, G., "Mr. Tompkins Explores the Atom," The University Press, Cambridge, England, 1944.

———"Mr. Tompkins in Wonderland," The Macmillan Company, New York, 1945.

Glasstone, S., "Sourcebook on Atomic Energy," 2nd ed., D. Van Nostrand Co., Inc., Princeton, N. J., 1958.

Halliday, D., "Introductory Nuclear Physics," 2nd ed., John Wiley & Sons, Inc., New York, 1955.

Lapp, R. E., and Andrews, H. L., "Nuclear Radiation Physics," 2nd ed., Prentice-Hall, Inc., Englewood Cliffs, N. J., 1954.

Price, W. J., "Nuclear Radiation Detection," McGraw-Hill Book Co., Inc., New York, 1958.

APPLICATIONS TO SPECIAL FIELDS

Boyd, G. A., "Autoradiography in Biology and Medicine," Academic Press, Inc., New York, 1955.

Comar, C. L., "Radioisotopes in Biology and Agriculture," McGraw-Hill Book Co., Inc., New York, 1955.

111

Kohl, J., Zentner, R. D., and Lukens, H. R., "Radioisotpe Applications Engineering," D. Van Nostrand Co., Inc., Princeton, N. J., 1961.

U. S. Department of Health, Education and Welfare, Division of Radiological Health, "Radiological Health Handbook," rev. ed., U. S. Dept. of Health, Education and Welfare, Washington, Sept., 1960 (PB-121784R).

Wahl, A. C., and Bonner, N. A., "Radioactivity Applied to Chemistry," John Wiley & Sons, Inc., New York, 1951.

INDEX

Absorption, exponential, 52
Absorption coefficient, 49
  Compton, 51
  and half-thickness, 85
  linear, 50
  mass, 50
  pair production, 51
  photoelectric process, 50
  total, 51
Absorption curve(s), 39
  background in, 40
  plotting, 41
Accuracy, 90
Actinide series, 100
Actinium series, natural radio-
    activity, 19
Activation analysis, 105
Activity
  in neutron bombardment, 106
  of radioactive daughter, 87
  specific, 105
Activity analysis, 103
Age dating, 107
Alpha decay, 19
Alpha emission, rate, 36
Annihilation photons, 49
Antineutrino, 32
Atomic number, 8
Average life, 85
  statistical nature, 80

Background
  in absorption curves, 40
  cosmic radiations in, 37
  from natural radioisotopes, 37
  pulses, 74
Barn, 106
Barrier model, potential, 22

Beta ray decay, 27
  and transuranium elements, 36
Beta ray spectra, 38
Binding energy, 11
  in fission, 98
Blood volume, by isotope
    dilution, 105
Bremsstrahlung, 45

Carrier-free samples
  in radioactivity, 103
  weight, 82
Chemical effects in radiation
    damage, 109
Compton effect, 48
Compton process in scintillation
    crystal, 71
Compton scattered radiation, 48
Containment, fusion, 99
Coulomb barrier, 17
Counter
  Geiger-Müller, 64, 70
  halogen-quenched, 65
  liquid scintillation, 73
  proportional, 64
  pulse, 66
  well, 76
Counting rate meter, 70
Critical amount, in fission
    process, 96
Cross section
  neutron, 106
  radiation, 49
Cumulative instruments, 66
Curie, 36
Current measurement, 66

Dating by carbon-14, 108

Dead time, 69
Decay
 alpha, 19
 beta ray, 27, 36
 radioactive, rate, 36
 radioactive daughter from, 85
Decay chains, 86
Decay laws, 80
Decay scheme, 35
Density thickness, 41
Deuterium, 8
 in fusion, 98
Deviation, 90
 standard, 92
Discharge, continuous, 63
Discriminator, 68
Disintegration constant, 81, 84
Disintegration scheme, 35
Disintegrations per second, 36
Dosimeters, 64
Dynodes, in photomultiplier tube, 75

E_{max}, 38
Electromagnetic radiation,
 38, 45
Electron capture, 33
 rate, 36
Electron motion, 2
Electron populations, 5
Electron shells, 4
Electron volt, 12
Electroscope, quartz fiber, 64
Emission
 alpha, rate, 36
 gamma, 31
Endoergic reactions, 13
 examples, 27
Energy levels, 4
 diagrams, 6
 nuclear, 33
Error
 accidental, 89
 definition, 90
 general sources, 89
 nine tenths, 92
 ninety-five hundredths, 92
 systematic, 89

Excitation, 42
 in scintillation crystal, 71
Excited nucleus, 26
Excited state, 25
Exoergic reactions, 13
 examples, 27
Extranuclear electron, 33

Fallout, 37
Fission, heat equivalent of, 98
Fission products, uranium, 27
Fission reaction, 95
Fission yield, 27
Flux, neutron, 106
Free radicals, in radiation
 damage, 110
Frequency of radiation, 45
Frequency distribution curve, 91
Fusion reactions, 95
 controlled, 98

Gamma emission, 31
Gamma ray spectrometry, 7,8
Gas
 amplification, 61
 quenching, 65
Geiger-Müller counter, 64, 70
Geiger region, 63
 instruments operating in, 64
Ground level, 30
Ground state, 34

Half life
 alpha, 24
 definition, 80
 derivation, 84
Half lives of mixture, 85
Half thickness, 52
 derivation, 85

Infinite life, 66
Input sensitivity, 68
Interactions
 "billiard-ball" collision, 48
 Compton process, 48, 71
 electromagnetic radiation, 45

excitation process, 42
pair production process, 48
particulate radiation, 41
Ion collection detectors, 58
Ionization, 43
primary, 61
secondary, 61
by secondary processes, 49
in scintillation crystal, 71
Ionization chamber, 64
Ion pair, 43
Isotope, 8
stable, tracing with, 18, 79, 104
Isotope dilution analysis, 104
Isotope effect, 108
Isotopic mass, 10

K electron capture (K capture), 33

Lanthanide series, 101
Light, velocity, 45
Liquid scintillation counters, 73

Magnetic bottles in fusion, 99
Mass defect, 11
Mass-energy equivalence
calculations, 11
in pair production, 48
Mass spectrometers
in determination of neutron-
proton masses, 10
use with tracers, 18, 79, 104
Maximum energy of beta radi-
ation, 38
Maximum permissible dose, 53
Mesonic charge, 16
mg/cm^2, 41
Model, 2
nuclear well, 24
potential barrier, 22
potential energy well, 17
shell, 17
Moderator, reactor, 97
Microcurie, 36
Millicurie, 36
Million electron volt, 12
Milliroentgen, 55

Multichannel analyzers, 78

Natural radioactivity, 19
in background, 37
Neutrino, 31
from electron capture, 33
Neutron-proton ratio
and alpha decay, 20
and beta decay, 29
high, in transuranium
elements, 36
low, in electron capture, 33
in positron emission, 34
and stability, 10
Noise, 67
in photomultiplier tubes, 74
Non-ionizing radiation, 46
Normal distribution law, 91
Nuclear chemistry, 1
Nuclear energy levels, 33
Nuclearity, 16
Nuclear radius, 14
Nuclear reactions, 24
Nuclear reactors, 97
Nuclear surface tension, 26
Nuclear well model, 24
Nuclide, 9
stable, 27

Ohm's law, 67

Pair production process, 48
in scintillation crystal, 71
Particulate radiation, 38, 41
Periodic table, 5
Personnel monitoring, 64
Phosphor, 72
Photoelectric process, 47
in scintillation crystal, 71
Photoelectron, 47
Photomultiplier tube, 72
operation, 74
Photons, 25
annihilation, 49
Photopeak, 78
Planck's constant, 46

Plasma, in fusion, 99
Plateau, in G-M counter, 70
Plutonium-239 fission, 96
Positive beta particle (positive electron, positron), 34
Potential barrier, 24
  model, 22
Potential energy well model, 17
Precision, 90
Proportional region, instruments operating in, 64
Pulse counters, 66
Pulse height
  definition, 68
  in G-M counters, 65
Pulse height analyzer, 76
  in activation analysis, 107
Pulse height selector, 76

Quantum mechanics
  in alpha decay, 22
  in electron distribution, 3
Quantum number, 4
Quartz fiber electroscopes, 64
Quenching gas, 65

rad, 54
Radiation chemistry, 109
Radiation damage, biological, 109
Radiation dosage, 53
Radiation shielding, 51
Radioactive daughter
  activity, 87
  decay to, 85
Radioactive decay, rate, 36
Radiochemistry
  applications, 104
  definitions, 1
Radioisotopes, 102
Radiometric analysis, 103
Radon, 37
Rate of drift, 67
RBE, 55
Recombination of ions, 43
Recovery time, 69
Relative biological effectiveness, 55

rem, 55
rep, 55
Resolving time, 65
Roentgen, 54
Roentgen equivalents, 55

Saturation voltage, 61
Scaling circuit, 69
Scintillation detection, 71
Secular equilibrium, 87
Shell model, 17
Single-channel analyzer, 78
Sodium iodide crystals, 72
Solid state detectors, 78
Space-charge effect, 62
Specific activity, 105
Spectra
  alpha, 39
  beta, 38
  gamma, 79
Spectrometers
  beta, 38
  gamma, 78
  mass, 10, 18, 79, 104
Stable isotopes, 10, 18, 79, 104
Stable nuclides, 27
Stability belt, 10
Standard deviation, 92
  of counting sample, 93
  differences in counting rates, 94
Sublevels, electron, 4

Target theory, 109
Thermonuclear device, 98
Thorium series, 19
Transmutation, 27
Transuranium elements, 101
Tritium, 8
Tunneling effect in quantum mechanics, 24

Uranium fission, 27, 96
Uranium series, 19

Velocity of light, 45

Wavelength of radiation, 45
Well counter, 76